Mathematics Progress Paper 16

C000028099

Q. 1–5	Write each of the following numbers in words.	
writing large numbers	**1** 1 720 000	1 ☐
	2 6 005 027	2 ☐
	3 12 400 400	3 ☐
	4 7 000 007	4 ☐
	5 26 070 430	5 ☐

Q. 6–10		
decimal addition and subtraction	**6** Add together 0.4, 0.04, 4.0 and 0.004.	6 ☐
	7 $11.207 + 6.03 + 0.4 + 0.039 =$	7 ☐
	8 Find the sum of 0.09, 0.904, 0.7 and 0.16.	8 ☐
	9 $\begin{array}{r} 276.32 \\ -\ 49.97 \\ \hline \end{array}$ **10** $\begin{array}{r} 864.220 \\ -\ 198.755 \\ \hline \end{array}$	9 ☐ 10 ☐

Q. 11–15		
decimal multiplication	**11** $7.638 \times 1000 =$	11 ☐
	12 $0.002 \times 1000 =$	12 ☐
	13 $0.7 \times 1000 =$	13 ☐
	14 $83.4 \times 0.006 =$	14 ☐
	15 $0.007 \times 0.004 =$	15 ☐

Q. 16–20		
decimal problems	**16** Subtract the difference between 1.0 and 0.1 from their sum.	16 ☐
	17 If 37.6 metres are cut from a rope $70\frac{1}{2}$ metres long, what length remains? _____ m	17 ☐
	18 If one euro is worth 17.55 yen, how many yen will you get for 65 euros? _____ yen	18 ☐
	19 The distance round a model train track is 4.68 m. How many metres will a train travel in forty laps? _____ m	19 ☐
	20 If a packet of sugar has a mass of 15.42 g, what will be the mass of 200 packets? _____ g	20 ☐

MARK ☐

MARK
✓ or ✗

Q. 21–25

Venn diagrams

Forty children were asked which comics they read. Put this information into the Venn diagram and then answer question 25.

21 5 read both the Beano and the Avengers.

22 18 read both the Beano and Batman.
Nobody reads all three comics.

23 7 read both Batman and the Avengers.

24 Nobody reads just the Avengers and 4 read only Batman.

25 How many children read only the Beano? _____

21 ☐

22 ☐

23 ☐

24 ☐

25 ☐

Batman   Beano

0

0

Avengers

Q. 26–30

fraction problems

26 Mr Hussain buys $1\frac{3}{4}$ kg of onions, $3\frac{1}{2}$ kg of potatoes and $\frac{7}{8}$ kg of cabbage. What total mass does he carry home? _____ kg

27 What fraction of 6 litres is 5 half litres? _____

28 Tom is nine years old and $1\frac{1}{2}$ times as old as his sister, Zoe. How old is Zoe? _____ years old

29 If a room is $6\frac{3}{5}$ m long and $3\frac{1}{4}$ m wide, what is the distance all round it? _____ m

30 How much is three-quarters of the product of seven-eighths and four-ninths? _____

26 ☐

27 ☐

28 ☐

29 ☐

30 ☐

Q. 31–35

factors and multiples

31 What is the highest common factor of 23 and 69? _____

32 What is the highest common factor of 24 and 60? _____

33 What is the lowest common multiple of 2 and 10? _____

34 What is the lowest common multiple of 4 and 12? _____

35 What is the lowest common multiple of 12 and 16? _____

31 ☐

32 ☐

33 ☐

34 ☐

35 ☐

MARK ☐

MARK
✓ or ✗

Q. 36–40

money problems

36 If I buy a car for £3060 and pay £85 per month for it, how long does it take me to pay for the car? _____ months

36 ☐

37 Eighty prize winners share £76 800. How much does each receive? £ _____

37 ☐

38 At a bring and buy sale, all books were sold for 80p each. If £448 was taken, how many books were sold? _____

38 ☐

39 Phoebe's new computer cost £648 and she paid for it in monthly instalments of £36. How many months did it take her to pay for it? _____ months

39 ☐

40 Two sisters and four brothers won £111 240. How much did they each receive? £ _____

40 ☐

Q. 41–45

measures addition and subtraction

41 $7.3 \text{ kg} + 1270 \text{ g} + 0.6 \text{ kg} + 4\frac{4}{5} \text{ kg} =$ _____ kg _____ g

41 ☐

42 £8.30 + £19.17 + £3.60 + £17 = £ _____

42 ☐

43 $2\frac{2}{3} \text{ h} + 43 \text{ min} + 1\frac{3}{5} \text{ h} + 126 \text{ min} + 420 \text{ sec} =$ _____ h _____ min

43 ☐

44 $12\,426 \text{ cm} - 93\frac{1}{4} \text{ m}$ _____ m _____ cm

44 ☐

45 $156.32 \text{ l} - 98\frac{19}{50} \text{ l} =$ _____ l _____ ml

45 ☐

Q. 46–50

reduce to lowest terms

Write these decimals as fractions in their lowest terms.

46 24.58 _____

46 ☐

47 3.05 _____

47 ☐

48 41.625 _____

48 ☐

49 36.44 _____

49 ☐

50 16.02 _____

50 ☐

Q. 51–55

capacity problems

51 Express 9500 cm³ as litres. _____ l

51 ☐

52 How many litres of milk are required for 220 pupils for four weeks if each pupil is allowed a $\frac{1}{4}$-litre bottle three times a week? _____ l

52 ☐

53 If water flows into a tank at the rate of seven litres per minute, how many litres will flow into the tank in 55 minutes? _____ l

53 ☐

54 Find the sum of 7.63 l, 128 590 ml and 0.05 l. _____ l _____ ml

54 ☐

55 How many litres are there in 720 $\frac{1}{2}$-litre bottles? _____ l

55 ☐

MARK ☐

MARK
✓ or ✗

Q. 56–60

time = distance ÷ speed

From the distance and speed given, work out the time taken.

	DISTANCE TRAVELLED	SPEED	TIME TAKEN	
56	240 kilometres	$1\frac{1}{4}$ km/h	_____ h	56 ☐
57	1392 kilometres	232 km/h	_____ h	57 ☐
58	396 kilometres	48 km/h	_____ h	58 ☐
59	612 kilometres	60 km/h	_____ h	59 ☐
60	100 metres	30 km/h	_____ s	60 ☐

Q. 61–65

graphs

This graph shows the profits made each year by a local cinema.

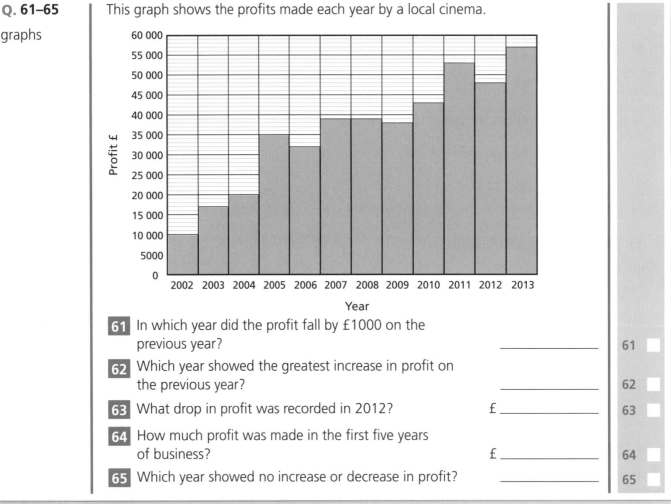

61 In which year did the profit fall by £1000 on the previous year? _____ 61 ☐

62 Which year showed the greatest increase in profit on the previous year? _____ 62 ☐

63 What drop in profit was recorded in 2012? £ _____ 63 ☐

64 How much profit was made in the first five years of business? £ _____ 64 ☐

65 Which year showed no increase or decrease in profit? _____ 65 ☐

Q. 66–70

volume

66 Convert $2\frac{1}{4}$ litres to cm³. _____ cm³ 66 ☐

67 Convert $4\frac{5}{8}$ litres to cm³. _____ cm³ 67 ☐

68 Convert 9.4 litres to cm³. _____ cm³ 68 ☐

69 Convert $12\frac{9}{10}$ litres to cm³. _____ cm³ 69 ☐

70 Convert 30.04 litres to cm³. _____ cm³ 70 ☐

MARK ☐

MARK
✓ or ✗

Q. 71–75	Write the next two terms in each of these sequences.							

sequences

71 11   14   19   26   _____   _____   71 ☐

72 $6\frac{1}{2}$ $9\frac{3}{4}$ 13 $16\frac{1}{4}$ _____   _____   72 ☐

73 25 mm   3 cm   35 mm   4 cm   _____   _____   73 ☐

74 7   8   11   12   15   _____   _____   74 ☐

75 0.5   0.9   1.5   2.3   _____   _____   75 ☐

Q. 76–80

ratio

Express each of these ratios in its lowest (simplest) form.

76 4 mm : 6 cm =   _____ : _____   76 ☐

77 $\frac{1}{4}$ s : $\frac{1}{2}$ min =   _____ : _____   77 ☐

78 6 min : $1\frac{1}{2}$ h =   _____ : _____   78 ☐

79 600 g : 2.4 kg =   _____ : _____   79 ☐

80 $3\frac{1}{2}$: $4\frac{1}{2}$: 1 =   _____ : _____ : _____   80 ☐

Q. 81–85

angles and degrees

Measure these angles.

81

∠ A = _____ °

82

∠ B = _____ °

83

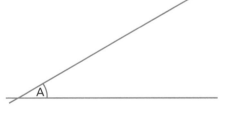

∠ C = _____ °

81 ☐

82 ☐

83 ☐

84 Which angle is acute?   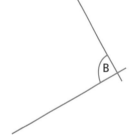   84 ☐

85 Which angle is obtuse?   85 ☐

MARK ☐

MARK
✓ or ✗

Q. 86–90

square numbers and roots

86 What is the square of 18? _____ | 86 ☐

87 From the square of 20 take the square of 17. _____ | 87 ☐

88 What is the square of $5\frac{1}{2}$? _____ | 88 ☐

89 What is the square root of 256? _____ | 89 ☐

90 From the square root of 361 take the square root of 16. _____ | 90 ☐

Q. 91–95

symmetry

Complete the pattern shown in each figure.
The dotted lines are lines of symmetry.

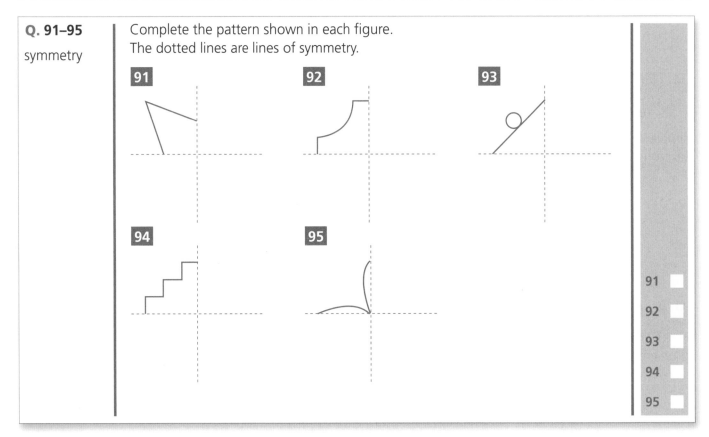

91 ☐

92 ☐

93 ☐

94 ☐

95 ☐

Q. 96–100

proportion

96 8 pens cost £4.48. How much would 23 pens cost? £ _____ | 96 ☐

97 Priya spends two-fifths of the day sleeping.
How long is she awake? _____ h _____ min | 97 ☐

98 Hayden spends $\frac{1}{3}$ of his money on sweets and $\frac{2}{5}$ of his money on magazines. If he has £2.32 left, how much money did he have to start with? £ _____ | 98 ☐

99 A flood at a shoe factory ruins $\frac{5}{8}$ of the stock. If 474 pairs of shoes were saved, how many were ruined? _____ | 99 ☐

100 Sarah gets twice as much pocket money as Lewis, who gets twice as much pocket money as Abbie. If they get £31.64 altogether, how much does Sarah get? £ _____ | 100 ☐

END OF TEST

TOTAL ☐

START HERE

Q. 1–5

simple addition and subtraction

1

```
  60 957
  38 698
  27 483
+ 99 865
_____
```

2

```
  97 428
  36 887
  42 663
+ 98 882
_____
```

3

```
  78 694
  33 862
  15 996
+ 87 986
_____
```

4

```
  8000
− 2754
_____
```

5

```
  5134
− 2984
_____
```

1	☐
2	☐
3	☐
4	☐
5	☐

Q. 6–10

simple division

6

$12 \overline{)70\ 152}$

7

$6 \overline{)25\ 776}$

8

$9 \overline{)807\ 777}$

9

$8 \overline{)6\ 374\ 680}$

10

$11 \overline{)4\ 135\ 428}$

6	☐
7	☐
8	☐
9	☐
10	☐

Q. 11–15

multiplication problems

11 One hundred and forty cartons each hold 72 eggs. How many eggs do they hold altogether? _____

12 A coach driver drives 700 km each week in the course of her work. If she has four weeks' holiday each year, how many km will she drive each year? _____ km

13 If 2 bakers produce forty-eight loaves of bread in an afternoon, how much bread could a hundred bakers produce? _____

14 Multiply the square of 36 by the product of five and seven. _____

15 How many hours are there in a year (not a leap year)? _____ h

11	☐
12	☐
13	☐
14	☐
15	☐

Q. 16–20

long multiplication

16 Multiply 432 by 5007. _____

17 What is the product of 2683 and 449? _____

18 £7.63 × 842 = £ _____

19 22 × 38 × 67 = _____

20 736 workers each received a bonus of £493.50. What was the total amount of money paid out? £ _____

16	☐
17	☐
18	☐
19	☐
20	☐

MARK ☐

MARK
✓ or ✗

Q. 21–25

translation

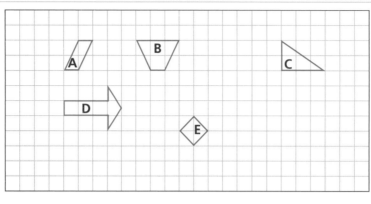

21 Translate shape A 3 squares to the left and 1 square up. Label it 1.

21 ☐

22 Translate shape B 2 squares down and 6 squares to the right. Label it 2.

22 ☐

23 Translate shape C 2 squares to the right and 1 square up. Label it 3.

23 ☐

24 Translate shape D 3 squares down and 3 squares to the left. Label it 4.

24 ☐

25 Translate shape E 3 squares to the right and 2 squares down. Label it 5.

25 ☐

Q. 26–30

decimal division

26 0.144 ÷ 1.2 = _____ 26 ☐

27 0.64 ÷ 0.008 = _____ 27 ☐

28 8.19 ÷ 9 = _____ 28 ☐

29 0.072 ÷ 0.08 = _____ 29 ☐

30 3.6 ÷ 0.12 = _____ 30 ☐

Q. 31–35

magic squares: fractions

		3
	2	
1	$2\frac{2}{3}$	

Complete this magic square.
Each column, row and diagonal should have the same total.

31 ☐
32 ☐
33 ☐
34 ☐
35 ☐

Q. 36–40

long division

36

$27\overline{)14\,769}$

37

$42\overline{)36\,372}$

38

$38\overline{)26\,676}$

39

$51\overline{)27\,489}$

40

$45\overline{)28\,080}$

36 ☐
37 ☐
38 ☐
39 ☐
40 ☐

MARK ☐

MARK
✓ or ✗

Q. 41–45

coordinates

A lifeboat is searching for a drifting yacht. Plot its course on this grid. Each centimetre on the grid equals one kilometre.

N

41 The lifeboat starts its search at point X and sails 4 km east. What are its coordinates now? (_____ , _____) | 41 ☐

42 It now sails 3 km due north and 7 km west. What are its coordinates now? (_____ , _____) | 42 ☐

43 An SOS is then received from point A. How far away is that? _____ km | 43 ☐

44 What are the coordinates of the distress call? (_____ , _____) | 44 ☐

45 After answering the distress call and rescuing the yacht, how far away is the lifeboat from point X where it began the search? _____ km | 45 ☐

Q. 46–50

percentage problems

46 If I get four and a half marks out of five in a test, what percentage is this? _____ % | 46 ☐

47 15% of 10 000 library books were damaged and thrown away. How many books were kept? _____ | 47 ☐

48 What is 181% of 1500? _____ | 48 ☐

49 What must be added to 119 to make it equal to $9\frac{1}{2}$% of 1400? _____ | 49 ☐

50 What is the value of half a per cent of £7000? £ _____ | 50 ☐

MARK ☐

MARK
✓ or ✗

Q. 51–55

measures
multiplication
and division

51 Multiply 8¼ days by 8. _____ d 51 ☐

52 22.083 l × 16 = _____ l _____ ml 52 ☐

53 27 680 mm × 3 = _____ m _____ cm 53 ☐

54 £2289.60 ÷ 18 = £ _____ 54 ☐

55 1243½ kg ÷ 5 = _____ kg _____ g 55 ☐

Q. 56–60

using money

This is a bill for food supplied to a sweet shop. Work out the total for each line so that they all add up to the total below.

	Harper's Stores Ltd	£ . p
56	4 dozen chocolate bars at 35p each	56 ☐
57	5 dozen lollipops at 27p each	57 ☐
58	6 dozen sherbert dips at 43p each	58 ☐
59	11 dozen cereal bars at 74p each	59 ☐
60	8 dozen packets of crisps at 39p each	60 ☐
	Total = 199.08	

Q. 61–65

money
problems

61 An aeroplane has 320 seats. If a flight to Egypt costs £150 and three-quarters of the seats are filled, how much money have the passengers paid in total? £ _____ 61 ☐

62 A book sells at £7.25 and the bookseller makes £1.50 profit. How much will he pay his suppliers for one hundred books? £ _____ 62 ☐

63 Multiply £423 by the product of eight and seven. £ _____ 63 ☐

64 A school buys 124 footballs costing £7.65 each, and 80 basketballs costing £8.30 each. How much does it spend altogether? £ _____ 64 ☐

65 Charlie is selling buns to raise money for charity. If he sells 843 buns at 15p each, how much money will he make? £ _____ 65 ☐

MARK ☐

MARK
✓ or ✗

Q. 66–70

BODMAS

66 17 (3 + 5) − 9 ÷ 3 = _____ 66 ☐

67 5 + 6 × 7 ÷ 21 = _____ 67 ☐

68 12 + 3³ × 2 = _____ 68 ☐

69 17 − 6 + 4 × 10 = _____ 69 ☐

70 19 × 3 + (14 ÷ 7) − 12 = _____ 70 ☐

Q. 71–75

time
problems

How many hours are there between these times?

71 1800 on Tuesday to 0300 on Thursday. _____ hours 71 ☐

72 1400 on Monday to 0900 on Thursday. _____ hours 72 ☐

73 0130 on Sunday to 2330 on Wednesday. _____ hours 73 ☐

74 1415 on Friday to 0245 on Monday. _____ hours 74 ☐

75 0100 on Saturday to 6 p.m. on Tuesday. _____ hours 75 ☐

Q. 76–80

triangles

How many degrees are there in the angle marked with a letter in each of these triangles?

76

∠ A = _____ °

77

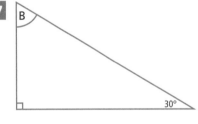

∠ B = _____ °

78

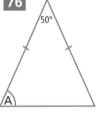

∠ C = _____ °

79

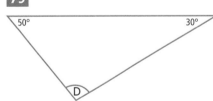

∠ D = _____ °

80

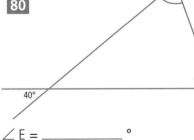

∠ E = _____ °

76 ☐
77 ☐
78 ☐
79 ☐
80 ☐

MARK ☐

MARK
✓ or ✗

Q. 81–85

division with remainders

Write the answers as decimals to one decimal place.

81 5291 ÷ 6 = _____ | 81 ☐

82 4536 ÷ 11 = _____ | 82 ☐

83 8574 ÷ 7 = _____ | 83 ☐

84 9324 ÷ 8 = _____ | 84 ☐

85 2736 ÷ 13 = _____ | 85 ☐

Q. 86–90

probability

If three coins are tossed in the air together, when they hit the ground either head (H) or tail (T) will be showing. Write H or T on each coin to show the different ways the coins could land. Three are done for you.

	COIN 1	COIN 2	COIN 3
86	T	T	H
87	T	H	H
88			
89			
90	H	H	H

86 ☐

87 ☐

88 ☐

89 ☐

90 ☐

MARK ☐

MARK
✓ or ✗

Q. 91–95

volume

91 1000 litres of water occupy 1 cubic metre. How many litres does a tank 5 m × 3 m × $2\frac{1}{2}$ m hold? _____ l

91 ☐

92 What is the volume of a small room $2\frac{1}{2}$ m high, 3 m long and 2 m wide? _____ m³

92 ☐

93 A box has a volume of 340 cubic centimetres. If it is 17 cm long and 4 cm high, how wide is it? _____ cm

93 ☐

94 A water tank measures 2 m by $4\frac{1}{2}$ m by 6 m. What volume of water does it hold? _____ m³

94 ☐

95 What is the volume of a cube with sides $4\frac{1}{2}$ cm long? _____ cm³

95 ☐

Q. 96–100

symmetry

How many lines of rotational symmetry do the following shapes have?

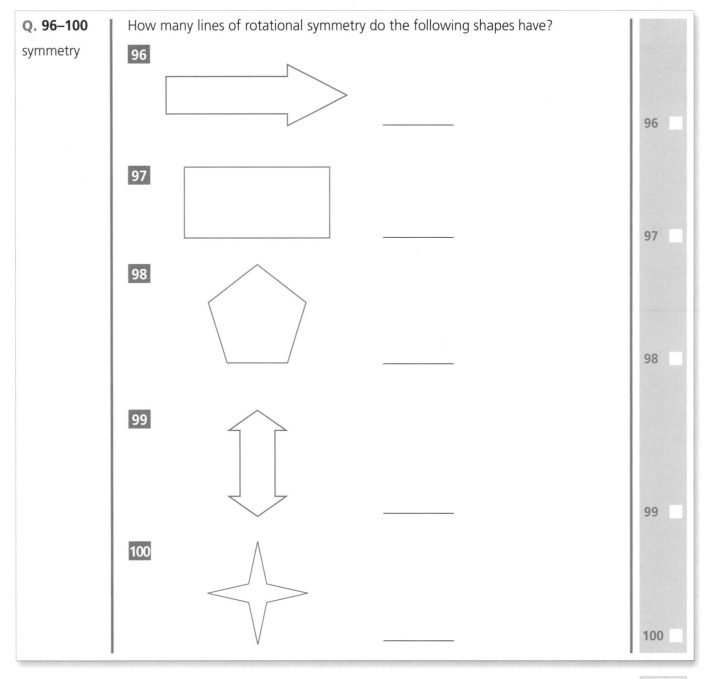

96 _____

96 ☐

97 _____

97 ☐

98 _____

98 ☐

99 _____

99 ☐

100 _____

100 ☐

END OF TEST

TOTAL ☐

Mathematics Progress Paper 18

MARK
✓ or ✗

Q. 1–5

measures addition and subtraction

1 5000 mm + 2100 cm + 7600 mm + 3890 cm = _____ m _____ cm

1 ☐

2 38.58 l + 23 $\frac{11}{20}$ l + 76 429 ml + 8$\frac{3}{4}$ l = _____ l _____ ml

2 ☐

3 3058p + 29p + 863p + 5p + 90 762p = £ _____

3 ☐

4 24 268 g − 9.7 kg = _____ kg _____ g

4 ☐

5 3$\frac{1}{4}$ h − 108 min = _____ h _____ min

5 ☐

Q. 6–10

money problems

6 A company's profit in the first four weeks of the year was £17 690, £18 655, £24 350 and £22 387. What was the total profit for that period? £ _____

6 ☐

7 Add seven-twentieths of a million pounds to five-eights of a million pounds. £ _____

7 ☐

8 To the sum of £80 097 and £63 759, add £27 440. £ _____

8 ☐

9 Add a half of £7500 to three-quarters of £18 000 and subtract their difference. £ _____

9 ☐

10 Miss Roberts went shopping with five twenty-pound notes in her purse. She came home with £18.32. How much had she spent? £ _____

10 ☐

Q. 11–15

length problems

This mileage chart gives the distance between various towns and cities.

Aberdeen															
578	Barnstaple														
176	440	Berwick-upon Tweed													
408	182	261	Birmingham												
484	93	347	87	Bristol											
445	240	291	100	148	Cambridge										
488	135	360	100	45	174	Cardiff									
212	364	90	194	272	258	274	Carlisle								
560	266	401	180	187	118	224	370	Dover							
120	452	56	285	365	326	366	92	440	Edinburgh						
555	40	420	160	74	218	119	345	241	440	Exeter					
147	558	190	388	455	451	471	194	560	132	545	Fort William				
142	453	100	286	362	352	371	92	460	42	440	102	Glasgow			
451	128	310	52	33	118	55	240	175	331	110	435	332	Gloucester		
432	145	305	52	50	140	55	220	203	315	125	417	315	28	Hereford	
425	300	300	150	208	244	192	214	330	306	285	410	308	182	160	Holyhead
104	615	215	444	520	485	525	250	594	157	590	66	168	490	470	465	Inverness
255	320	130	147	225	215	230	45	322	137	302	242	140	193	175	165	295	Kendal

Write down the distance between:

11 Barnstaple and Holyhead. _____ miles

11 ☐

12 Exeter and Fort William. _____ miles

12 ☐

13 Birmingham and Glasgow. _____ miles

13 ☐

14 Hereford and Berwick-upon-Tweed. _____ miles

14 ☐

15 Cardiff and Kendal. _____ miles

15 ☐

MARK ☐

Schofield & Sims • Progress Papers • Mathematics 3

MARK
✓ or ✗

Q. 16–20

24-hour clock

Change the times shown on these digital clocks to a.m. or p.m. times.
Don't forget to write a.m. or p.m. after each one.

16 | 1 | 7 | 3 | 0 | **17** | 1 | 3 | 5 | 0 | **18** | 1 | 6 | 2 | 5 |

_____   _____   _____

19 | 0 | 0 | 2 | 0 | **20** | 2 | 3 | 0 | 4 |

_____   _____

16 ☐
17 ☐
18 ☐
19 ☐
20 ☐

Q. 21–25

fractions to decimals

Convert the following fractions into decimals.

21 $\frac{12}{25}$ =   _____

22 $\frac{7}{20}$ =   _____

23 $\frac{7}{8}$ =   _____

24 $\frac{37}{50}$ =   _____

25 $\frac{6}{16}$ =   _____

21 ☐
22 ☐
23 ☐
24 ☐
25 ☐

Q. 26–30

measures multiplication and division

26 $76\frac{41}{50}$ l × 13 =   _____ l   _____ ml

27 2500 g × 18 =   _____ kg

28 Divide £3943.62 by 27.   £ _____

29 $11\frac{3}{10}$ km ÷ 100 =   _____ m

30 1256 days ÷ 8 =   _____ wk   _____ d

26 ☐
27 ☐
28 ☐
29 ☐
30 ☐

Q. 31–35

compass points

31 Arya faces east. She turns 315° anticlockwise then 135° clockwise. In which direction is she now facing?   _____

32 Fran faces south east. She turns 225° anticlockwise and then 270° anticlockwise. She wants to face south west. How many degrees clockwise will she now need to turn?   _____

33 Malik faces west. He makes two complete turns clockwise, a half turn anticlockwise and then turns 90° clockwise. In which direction is he now facing?   _____

34 Lila faces north east. She turns 135° anticlockwise, 90° clockwise and then 225° anticlockwise. She wants to face north. How many degrees anticlockwise will she now need to turn?   _____

35 James turns 90° clockwise, 225° anticlockwise, 270° anticlockwise and 45° clockwise. He ends up facing south west. In which direction was he facing at the start?   _____

31 ☐
32 ☐
33 ☐
34 ☐
35 ☐

MARK [   ]

MARK
✓ or ✗

Q. 36–40

scale

This is a map of the centre of Moortown.   Scale 1 cm = 100 m

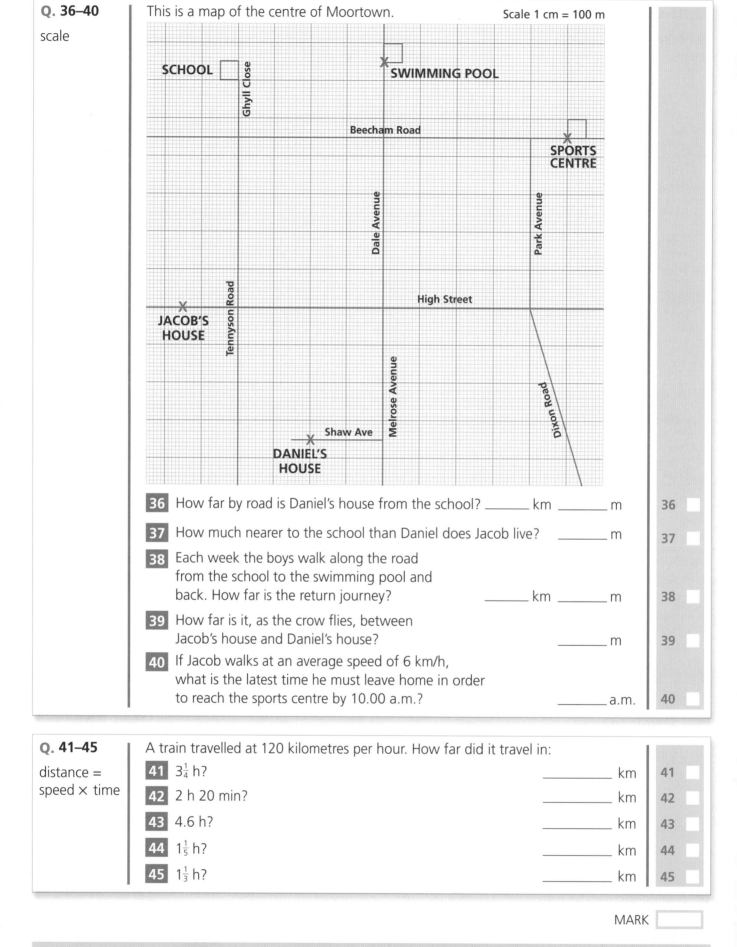

36 How far by road is Daniel's house from the school? _____ km _____ m   36 ☐

37 How much nearer to the school than Daniel does Jacob live?   _____ m   37 ☐

38 Each week the boys walk along the road
from the school to the swimming pool and
back. How far is the return journey?   _____ km _____ m   38 ☐

39 How far is it, as the crow flies, between
Jacob's house and Daniel's house?   _____ m   39 ☐

40 If Jacob walks at an average speed of 6 km/h,
what is the latest time he must leave home in order
to reach the sports centre by 10.00 a.m.?   _____ a.m.   40 ☐

Q. 41–45

distance =
speed × time

A train travelled at 120 kilometres per hour. How far did it travel in:

41 $3\frac{1}{4}$ h?   _____ km   41 ☐

42 2 h 20 min?   _____ km   42 ☐

43 4.6 h?   _____ km   43 ☐

44 $1\frac{1}{5}$ h?   _____ km   44 ☐

45 $1\frac{1}{3}$ h?   _____ km   45 ☐

MARK ☐

MARK
✓ or ✗

Q. 46–50

shape properties

Which of these shapes would not tessellate?

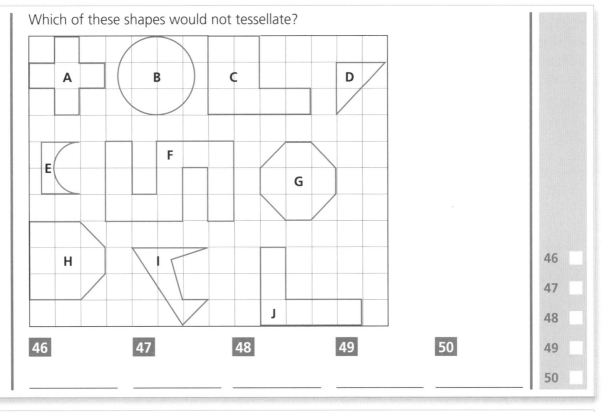

| 46 | 47 | 48 | 49 | 50 |

46 ☐
47 ☐
48 ☐
49 ☐
50 ☐

17

Q. 51–55

triangles

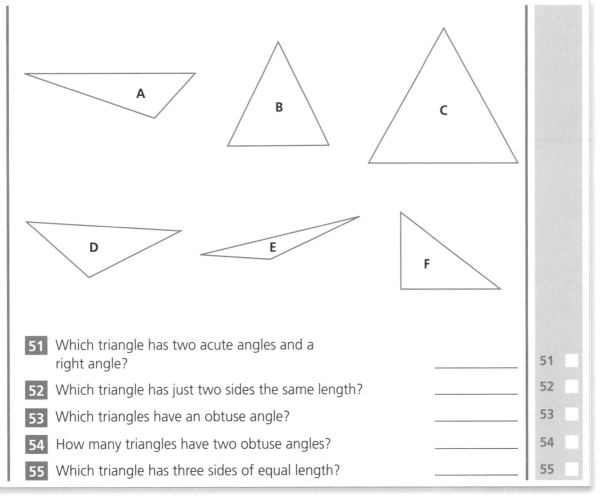

51 Which triangle has two acute angles and a right angle? _____

52 Which triangle has just two sides the same length? _____

53 Which triangles have an obtuse angle? _____

54 How many triangles have two obtuse angles? _____

55 Which triangle has three sides of equal length? _____

51 ☐
52 ☐
53 ☐
54 ☐
55 ☐

MARK ☐

MARK
✓ or ✗

Q. 56–60

percentage problems

Convert Emma's exam results into percentages.

	Subject	Mark	Percentage
56	maths	15/20	_____ %
57	English	37/50	_____ %
58	science	27/30	_____ %
59	geography	42/60	_____ %
60	history	56/70	_____ %

56 ☐
57 ☐
58 ☐
59 ☐
60 ☐

Q. 61–65

nets

Which of these nets could make a cube if they were cut out and folded?

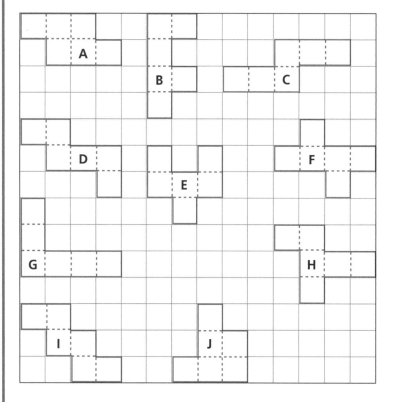

61 ☐
62 ☐
63 ☐
64 ☐
65 ☐

61	62	63	64	65
_____	_____	_____	_____	_____

MARK ☐

MARK
✓ or ✗

Q. 66–70

mean,
median,
mode and
range

66 The mean mass of 12 dogs was 42 kg.
What was their total mass? _____ kg | 66 ☐

67 Find the mean of these weekly wages:
£187.50, £293.50 and £176.60. £ _____ | 67 ☐

68 What is the mean of 590, 595 and 600? _____ | 68 ☐

69 Find the mean of $\frac{1}{2}$, $\frac{1}{3}$, $\frac{1}{4}$ and $\frac{1}{6}$. _____ | 69 ☐

70 What is the mean number of days in a month in
a leap year? Give your answer as a decimal. _____ | 70 ☐

Q. 71–75

unequal
sharing

71 £300 is shared out among four people so that Hamza
gets £20 more than each of the others. How much
does Hamza get? £ _____ | 71 ☐

72 Divide £648 between two people so that one gets
$1\frac{1}{4}$ times as much as the other. How much is the
greater share? £ _____ | 72 ☐

73 Divide £407 between two people so that one gets
$1\frac{1}{5}$ times as much as the other. How much is the
greater share? £ _____ | 73 ☐

74 Divide £380 between two people so that one gets
$1\frac{3}{8}$ times as much as the other. How much is
the greater share? £ _____ | 74 ☐

75 Share £70 among three people so that Lauren gets
$1\frac{1}{3}$ times as much as each of the others. How much
is the largest share? £ _____ | 75 ☐

Q. 76–80

decimal long
multiplication

76
$$0.0426 \times 2.7$$

77
$$0.0058 \times 0.47$$

78
$$0.0079 \times 0.63$$

| 76 ☐
| 77 ☐
| 78 ☐

79 $173.85 \times 0.62 =$ _____ | 79 ☐

80 $38.429 \times 18 =$ _____ | 80 ☐

Q. 81–85

decimal
long division

81 $0.935 \div 0.25 =$ _____ | 81 ☐

82 $5.439 \div 3.7 =$ _____ | 82 ☐

83 $258.85 \div 3.1 =$ _____ | 83 ☐

84 $2.6676 \div 0.57 =$ _____ | 84 ☐

85 $6.2712 \div 0.36 =$ _____ | 85 ☐

MARK ☐

MARK
✓ or ✗

Q. 86–90

number lines

Write the value of each letter as a decimal.

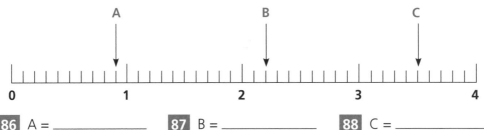

86 A = _____   87 B = _____   88 C = _____

Write the value of each letters as a mixed number.

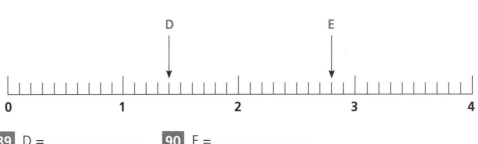

89 D = _____   90 E = _____

86 ☐
87 ☐
88 ☐

89 ☐
90 ☐

Q. 91–95

algebra

If $a = 6$, $b = 2$ and $c = 1$, solve the following equations:

91 $3a + b =$ _____

92 $2b - c =$ _____

93 $a + 3b =$ _____

94 $2b - 2c =$ _____

95 $a - b - c =$ _____

91 ☐
92 ☐
93 ☐
94 ☐
95 ☐

Q. 96–100

reduce to
lowest terms

96 Write the improper fraction $\frac{28}{6}$ as a mixed number in its lowest terms. _____

97 Write the improper fraction $\frac{52}{7}$ as a mixed number in its lowest terms. _____

98 Write the improper fraction $\frac{104}{24}$ as a mixed number in its lowest terms. _____

99 Write $4\frac{3}{5}$ as an improper fraction. _____

100 Write $7\frac{5}{6}$ as an improper fraction. _____

96 ☐
97 ☐
98 ☐
99 ☐
100 ☐

END OF TEST

TOTAL ☐

MARK
✓ or ✗

Q. 1–5

timetables

The Keighley and Worth Valley Railway is a private railway, five miles long, in West Yorkshire. This is their timetable for Saturdays throughout the year.

		D	D	☕	☕	☕	☕	☕
Oxenhope	d	0920	1035	1110	1230	1350	1520	1645
Haworth	d	0926	1040	1116	1236	1356	1526	1651
Oakworth	d	0929	1043	1119	1239	1359	1529	1654
Damems	**R**	**0932**	**1046**	**1122**	**1242**	**1402**	**1532**	**1657**
Ingrow West	d	0934	1048	1125	1245	1405	1535	1700
Keighley	a	0945	1055	1135	1255	1415	1545	1710

		D	D	☕	☕	☕	☕	
Keighley	d	1005	1115	1150	1310	1435	1605	1725
Ingrow West	d	1009	1119	1155	1315	1440	1610	1730
Damems	**R**	**1011**	**1121**	**1157**	**1317**	**1442**	**1612**	**1732**
Oakworth	d	1015	1125	1203	1323	1448	1618	1738
Haworth	d	1020	1130	1208	1328	1453	1623	1743
Oxenhope	a	1026	1136	1215	1335	1500	1630	1750

D = diesel train

☕ = steam train and buffet car

1 Which train from Oxenhope to Keighley completes the journey in the shortest time? _____ | 1 ☐

2 Which is the last train leaving Keighley on which food is available? _____ | 2 ☐

3 If I have an appointment in Keighley at 1530, which is the latest train leaving Oakworth that would get me there on time? _____ | 3 ☐

4 If the average time for the whole journey is 25 minutes, what is the train's average speed in miles per hour (mph)? _____ mph | 4 ☐

5 The station manager at Oakworth begins his day at 0900. One of his duties is to close the level crossing gates. If he goes home two minutes after closing the gates for the last time, how long is his working day? _____ h _____ min | 5 ☐

Q. 6–10

division problems

6 If £1 is worth 1.46 US dollars, how many pounds have to be changed in order to receive 73 dollars? £ _____ | 6 ☐

7 A farmer's hens produced 44 268 eggs in one week. How many eggs, on average, were produced per day? _____ | 7 ☐

8 How many minutes are there in 2280 seconds? _____ min | 8 ☐

9 How much money will each receive if £5400 is divided equally among 15 people? £ _____ | 9 ☐

10 A school library has 23 450 books for its 350 pupils. How many books per pupil is this? _____ | 10 ☐

Q. 11–15

fraction multiplication and division

11 $7\frac{3}{5} \times 3 =$ _____ | 11 ☐

12 $9\frac{3}{8} \times 6 =$ _____ | 12 ☐

13 $3\frac{1}{5} \times 4 =$ _____ | 13 ☐

14 $4\frac{1}{3} \div 2 =$ _____ | 14 ☐

15 $4\frac{1}{2} \div 4 =$ _____ | 15 ☐

MARK ☐

MARK
✓ or ✗

Q. 16–20

large number problems

This diagram shows the estimated distance of each planet (including dwarf planet, Pluto), in kilometres from the Sun.

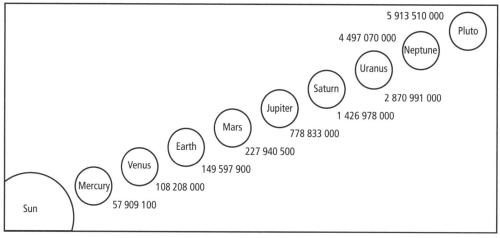

5 913 510 000	Pluto	
4 497 070 000	Neptune	
2 870 991 000	Uranus	
1 426 978 000	Saturn	
778 833 000	Jupiter	
227 940 500	Mars	
149 597 900	Earth	
108 208 000	Venus	
57 909 100	Mercury	
	Sun	

16 How much further from the Sun is Mars than is Earth?   _____ km | 16 ☐ |

17 How much further from the Sun is Pluto than is Earth?   _____ km | 17 ☐ |

18 How much further from the Sun is Mars than is Mercury?   _____ km | 18 ☐ |

19 Take the distance between the Sun and the nearest planet from the distance between the Sun and the furthest.   _____ km | 19 ☐ |

20 How much further from the Sun is Uranus than is Venus?   _____ km | 20 ☐ |

Q. 21–25

fractions to percentages

Change each of these fractions to a percentage.

21 $5\frac{1}{3}$ = _____ %   **22** $4\frac{5}{8}$ = _____ %   **23** $3\frac{4}{5}$ = _____ %

24 $7\frac{7}{25}$ = _____ %   **25** 8 = _____ %

| 21 ☐ |
| 22 ☐ |
| 23 ☐ |
| 24 ☐ |
| 25 ☐ |

Q. 26–30

number lines

Write the value of each letter as a mixed number.

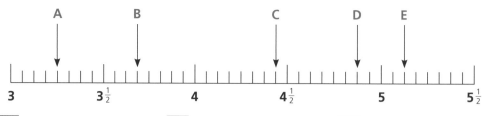

26 A = _____   **27** B = _____   **28** C = _____

29 D = _____   **30** E = _____

| 26 ☐ |
| 27 ☐ |
| 28 ☐ |
| 29 ☐ |
| 30 ☐ |

MARK ☐

MARK
✓ or ✗

Q. 31–35

probability

In a box there are 6 green balls, 5 red balls, 2 yellow balls, a purple ball, 8 orange balls and 2 blue balls. What is the probability of taking the following from the box:

31 a green ball? _____ 31 ☐

32 a purple ball? _____ 32 ☐

33 a red or purple ball? _____ 33 ☐

34 an orange ball? _____ 34 ☐

35 a blue or yellow ball? _____ 35 ☐

Q. 36–40

mass problems

A grocer goes to his wholesaler for supplies. So that he does not overload his small van, he asks the wholesaler to give him a list of the items he has bought together with their masses. Work out the individual masses so that they add up to the total given below.

Quality and Quantity Wholesale Grocery Supplies

kg　　g

36 200 bags of rice at 300 g each　　　　　36 ☐

37 300 jars of chocolate spread at 454 g each　　37 ☐

38 400 boxes of sweets at 250 g each　　　　38 ☐

39 700 boxes of muesli at 500 g each　　　　39 ☐

40 300 packets of biscuits at 225 g each _____　40 ☐

Total =　7 1 3　7 0 0

Q. 41–45

length problems

41 5cm of steel wire is needed to make 3 pins. How many pins can be made from 120 metres of wire? _____ 41 ☐

42 How many measuring tapes, each $1\frac{1}{4}$ metres long, can be made from a roll of tape $1\frac{1}{4}$ km long? _____ 42 ☐

43 Subtract one-twelfth of 60 kilometres from 17 500 metres. _____ km _____ m 43 ☐

44 Builders are laying new kerbstones, each 1 m 40 cm long. If they lay 72 altogether, what is the total length of the new kerb? _____ m _____ cm 44 ☐

45 Multiply $12\frac{7}{8}$ km by 6 and divide your answer by two. _____ km _____ m 45 ☐

MARK ☐

MARK
✓ or ✗

Q. 46–50

shape
properties

46 If the diameter of a circle is 9 cm, what is its radius? _____ cm | 46 ☐

47 The radius of a circle is 26.5 mm. What is the diameter? _____ mm | 47 ☐

48 The radius of a circle is the square root of 25 cm.
What is its diameter? _____ cm | 48 ☐

49 A circle's diameter, in cm, measures 4^3. What is its radius? _____ cm | 49 ☐

50 When multiplied by 3.5, the radius of a circle measures
63 mm. What is its diameter? _____ mm | 50 ☐

Q. 51–55

speed =
distance ÷
time

51 A car travels $262\frac{1}{2}$ kilometres in $3\frac{1}{2}$ hours.
What is its average speed? _____ km/h | 51 ☐

52 A plane flew 2945 km in $4\frac{3}{4}$ hours.
At what speed was it flying? _____ km/h | 52 ☐

53 A walker covered $31\frac{1}{2}$ km in 9 hours.
What was her average speed? _____ km/h | 53 ☐

54 If I drive 192 metres in 12 seconds, what speed is
this in km/h? _____ km/h | 54 ☐

55 540 metres in 6 minutes is what speed per hour? _____ km/h | 55 ☐

Q. 56–60

divisibility
rules

56 Circle the numbers which are divisible by 3, 4 and 9.
240   648   333   972   144 | 56 ☐

57 Circle the numbers which are divisible by 3, 5 and 9.
135   540   312   415   765 | 57 ☐

58 Circle the numbers which are divisible by 2, 5 and 9.
720   460   280   450   810 | 58 ☐

Complete the following sums by using your knowledge of divisibility rules:

59 ___ × ___ × ___ = 459 | 59 ☐

60 ___ × ___ × ___ = 285 | 60 ☐

Q. 61–65

magic
squares

Fill in the missing numbers in this square so that all the lines, down,
across and diagonal, add up to the same number.

5		9
	6	
		7

| 61 ☐
| 62 ☐
| 63 ☐
| 64 ☐
| 65 ☐

MARK ☐

Progress Papers
Answers

Mathematics 3

Schofield & Sims

Progress Paper 16

1	one million seven hundred and twenty thousand
2	six million five thousand and twenty-seven
3	twelve million four hundred thousand four hundred
4	seven million and seven
5	twenty-six million seventy thousand four hundred and thirty
6	4.444
7	17.676
8	1.854
9	226.35
10	665.465
11	7638
12	2
13	700
14	0.5004
15	0.000028
16	0.2
17	32.9 m
18	1140.75 yen
19	187.2 m
20	3084 g
21–24	

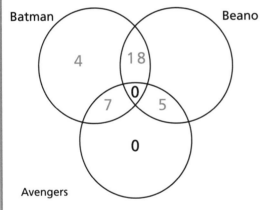

25	6
26	$6\frac{1}{8}$ kg
27	$\frac{5}{12}$
28	6 years old
29	$19\frac{7}{10}$ m
30	$\frac{7}{24}$
31	23
32	12
33	10
34	12
35	48

Paper 16 – continued

36	36 months
37	£960
38	560
39	18 months
40	£18 540
41	13 kg 970 g
42	£48.07
43	7 h 12 min
44	31 m 1 cm
45	57 l 940 ml
46	$24\frac{29}{50}$
47	$3\frac{1}{20}$
48	$41\frac{5}{8}$
49	$36\frac{11}{25}$
50	$16\frac{1}{50}$
51	9.5 l
52	660 l
53	385 l
54	136 l 270 ml
55	360 l
56	192 h
57	6 h
58	$8\frac{1}{4}$ h
59	$10\frac{1}{5}$ h
60	12 s
61	2009
62	2005
63	£5000
64	£114 000
65	2008
66	2250 cm³
67	4625 cm³
68	9400 cm³
69	12 900 cm³
70	30 040 cm³
71	35, 46
72	$19\frac{1}{2}$, $22\frac{3}{4}$,
73	45 mm, 5 cm
74	16, 19
75	3.3, 4.5

Paper 16 – *continued*

76	1 : 15
77	1 : 120
78	1 : 15
79	1 : 4
80	7 : 9 : 2
81	30°
82	90°
83	160°
84	A
85	C
86	324
87	111
88	$30\frac{1}{4}$
89	16
90	15

91

92

93

94

95

Paper 16 – *continued*

96	£12.88
97	14 h 24 min
98	£8.70
99	790
100	£18.08

Progress Paper 17

1	227 003
2	275 860
3	216 538
4	5246
5	2150
6	5846
7	4296
8	89 753
9	796 835
10	375 948
11	10 080
12	33 600 km
13	2400
14	45 360
15	8760 h
16	2 163 024
17	1 204 667
18	£6424.46
19	56 012
20	£363 216

21–25

Paper 17 – continued

26	0.12
27	80
28	0.91
29	0.9
30	30

31–35

$1\frac{2}{3}$	$1\frac{1}{3}$	3
$3\frac{1}{3}$	2	$\frac{2}{3}$
1	$2\frac{2}{3}$	$2\frac{1}{3}$

36	547
37	866
38	702
39	539
40	624
41	(11 , 5)
42	(4 , 8)
43	7 km
44	(4 , 1)
45	5 km
46	90%
47	8500
48	2715
49	14
50	£35
51	66 d
52	353 l 328 ml
53	83 m 4 cm
54	£127.20
55	248 kg 700 g
56	£16.80
57	£16.20
58	£30.96
59	£97.68
60	£37.44
61	£36 000
62	£575
63	£23 688
64	£1612.60
65	£126.45

Paper 17 – *continued*

66	133
67	7
68	66
69	51
70	47
71	33 hours
72	67 hours
73	94 hours
74	$60\frac{1}{2}$ hours
75	89 hours
76	65°
77	60°
78	60°
79	100°
80	70°
81	881.8
82	412.4
83	1224.9
84	1165.5
85	210.5

86

87

88

89

90

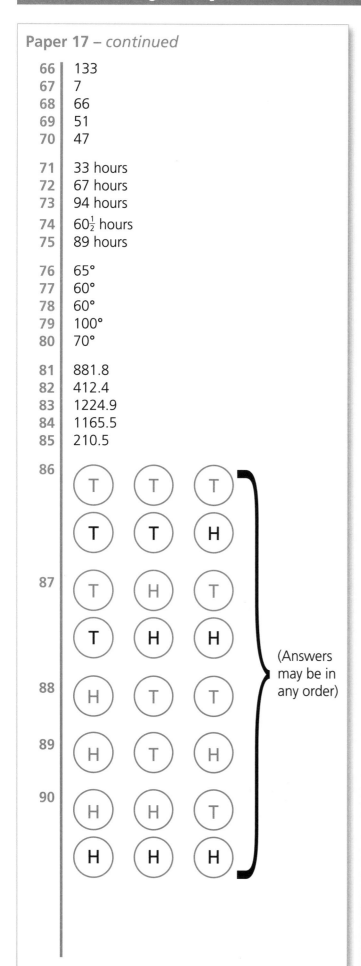

(Answers may be in any order)

Paper 17 – *continued*

91	37 500 l
92	15 m³
93	5 cm
94	54 m³
95	$91\frac{1}{8}$ cm³
96	1
97	2
98	5
99	2
100	4

Progress Paper 18

1	72 m 50 cm
2	147 l 309 ml
3	£947.17
4	14 kg 568 g
5	1 h 27 min
6	£83 082
7	£975 000
8	£171 296
9	£6750
10	£81.68
11	300 miles
12	545 miles
13	286 miles
14	305 miles
15	230 miles
16	5.30 p.m.
17	1.50 p.m.
18	4.25 p.m.
19	12.20 a.m.
20	11.04 p.m.
21	0.48
22	0.35
23	0.875
24	0.74
25	0.375
26	998 l 660 ml
27	45 kg
28	£146.06
29	113 m
30	22 wk 3 d
31	west
32	225°
33	south
34	135°
35	south west
36	1 km 550 m
37	800 m
38	1 km 500 m
39	500 m
40	9.45 a.m.
41	390 km
42	280 km
43	552 km
44	144 km
45	160 km

Paper 18 – *continued*

46	B
47	E
48	G
49	H
50	I

(Answers may be in any order)

51	triangle F
52	triangle B
53	triangles A, D, E
54	none
55	triangle C
56	75%
57	74%
58	90%
59	70%
60	80%

61	C
62	D
63	F
64	H
65	I

(Answers may be in any order)

66	504 kg
67	£219.20
68	595
69	$\frac{5}{16}$
70	30.5
71	£90
72	£360
73	£222
74	£220
75	£28
76	0.11502
77	0.002726
78	0.004977
79	107.787
80	691.722
81	3.74
82	1.47
83	83.5
84	4.68
85	17.42
86	0.9
87	2.2
88	3.5
89	$1\frac{2}{5}$
90	$2\frac{4}{5}$

Paper 18 – *continued*

91	20
92	3
93	12
94	2
95	3
96	$4\frac{2}{3}$
97	$7\frac{3}{7}$
98	$4\frac{1}{3}$
99	$\frac{23}{5}$
100	$\frac{47}{6}$

Progress Paper 19

1	1035
2	1605
3	1359
4	12 mph
5	8 h 40 min
6	£50
7	6324
8	38 min
9	£360
10	67
11	$22\frac{4}{5}$
12	$56\frac{1}{4}$
13	$12\frac{4}{5}$
14	$2\frac{1}{6}$
15	$1\frac{1}{8}$
16	78 342 600 km
17	5 763 912 100 km
18	170 031 400 km
19	5 855 600 900 km
20	2 762 783 000 km
21	$533\frac{1}{3}\%$
22	$462\frac{1}{2}\%$
23	380%
24	728%
25	800%
26	$3\frac{1}{4}$
27	$3\frac{11}{16}$
28	$4\frac{7}{16}$
29	$4\frac{7}{8}$
30	$5\frac{1}{8}$
31	$\frac{1}{4}$
32	$\frac{1}{24}$
33	$\frac{1}{4}$
34	$\frac{1}{3}$
35	$\frac{1}{6}$

	kg	g
36	60	0
37	136	200
38	100	0
39	350	0
40	67	500

Paper 19 – *continued*

41	7200
42	1000
43	12 km 500 m
44	100 m 80 cm
45	38 km 625 m
46	4.5 cm
47	53 mm
48	10 cm
49	32 cm
50	36 mm
51	75 km/h
52	620 km/h
53	$3\frac{1}{2}$ km/h
54	57.6 km/h
55	5.4 km/h
56	648, 972, 144
57	135, 540, 765
58	720, 450, 810
59	$9 \times 3 \times 17$
60	$5 \times 3 \times 19$

61–65

5	4	9
10	6	2
3	8	7

66	500
67	625 000 l
68	65
69	800 m
70	12 000
71	120 cm
72	84 cm
73	108 cm
74	8 m
75	194 m
76	$12\frac{11}{16}$ m²
77	20 m²
78	£18
79	54 cm²
80	216 cm²

Paper 19 – *continued*

81	81 years
82	171 years
83	443 years
84	1113 years
85	2559 years
	(Please note that there is no year 0 BCE or CE 0 – the year 1 BCE is followed by CE 1)
86	5 m
87	6 cm
88	4 cm
89	11 cm
90	11 m

91–95

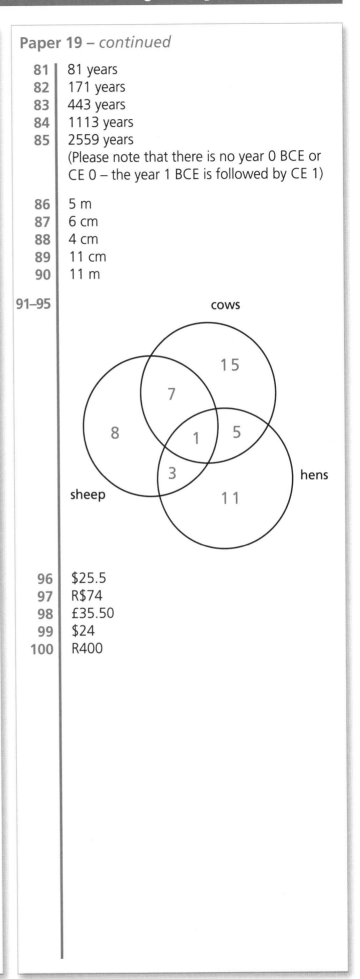

96	$25.5
97	R$74
98	£35.50
99	$24
100	R400

Progress Paper 20

1	Class A: 20 books
2	Class B: 28 books
3	Class C: 38 books
4	Class D: 34 books
5	Class E: 24 books
6	8 300 000
7	7 375 000
8	15 750 000
9	19 050 000
10	32 600 000
11	3520
12	0.469
13	77.136
14	80.52
15	331.2504
16	4
17	9
18	2
19	7
20	23
21	1000 cm²
22	800 cm²
23	250 cm²
24	0.28 m²
25	14
26	19 h 29 min
27	2 kg 559 g
28	2 km 710 m
29	£11 557.69
30	99 l 110 ml
31	£408.75
32	£620.00
33	£760.00
34	£1345.50
35	£1532.20

Paper 20 – *continued*

36	Shape V: 3, 12
37	Shape W: 10, 13
38	Shape X: 9, 8
39	Shape Y: 3, 4
40	Shape Z: 11, 3
41	£765
42	£654
43	£8530
44	£86 450
45	£10
46	630%
47	987.5%
48	$766\frac{2}{3}$%
49	500%
50	1248%
51	13°F
52	15°F
53	26°F
54	7
55	74°F
56	9 h 0 min
57	3 h 45 min
58	18 h 40 min
59	5 h 25 min
60	26 h 30 min
61	3 s
62	$4\frac{3}{4}$ h
63	$6\frac{1}{2}$ h
64	$10\frac{3}{4}$ h
65	$7\frac{1}{2}$ d

Paper 20 – *continued*

66	0.0076, 0.067, 0.0764, 0.6, 0.67
67	0.03, 0.033, 0.3, 0.303, 0.33
68	0.115, 0.15, 0.501, 0.51, 0.515
69	0.23, 0.293, 0.32, 0.329, 0.392
70	0.484, 0.845, 0.85, 0.853, 0.89
71	−31
72	−19
73	−71
74	−54
75	−88
76	$\frac{5}{2}$, 1
77	625, 1296
78	−4, −12
79	XLVII, LV
80	65.8, 79.6
81	60 min
82	£6.80
83	300°
84	£27
85	290 km
86	30p and 210p
87	10 m and 1.25 m
88	£32.55 : £13.95 : £4.65
89	14 kg 100 g : 9 kg 400 g : 4 kg 700 g
90	59 km 200 m : 22 km 200 m
91	60°
92	90°
93	95°
94	18°
95	360°
96	A and I
97	B and E
98	C and H
99	D and G
100	F and J

96–100 (Answers may be in any order)

Progress Paper 21

1	1 124 000
2	460 000
3	4 572 600
4	620 000
5	9 500 000
6	$48\frac{9}{20}$
7	$33\frac{35}{48}$
8	$34\frac{5}{36}$
9	$1\frac{1}{3}$
10	$9\frac{4}{5}$
11	7060 g
12	4003 ml
13	8090 m
14	11 480 g
15	5040 min

16–20

14	7	12	1
11	2	13	8
5	16	3	10
4	9	6	15

21	157.5 cm²
22	351 cm²
23	115 cm²
24	315 cm²
25	1755 cm²
26	387
27	862
28	730
29	611
30	2764
31	<
32	>
33	<
34	=
35	=
36	198 m
37	90 m
38	2300 m²
39	400 m²
40	1900 m²

Paper 21 – *continued*

41	£177.60
42	£275.20
43	£2964
44	£696
45	£457.60
46	20 000
47	30
48	24 000
49	100
50	80 000
51	$\frac{2}{9}$ $\frac{2}{5}$ $\frac{3}{7}$ $\frac{5}{8}$ $\frac{4}{5}$
52	$\frac{2}{7}$ $\frac{2}{6}$ $\frac{7}{10}$ $\frac{8}{11}$ $\frac{3}{4}$
53	$\frac{4}{8}$ $\frac{4}{7}$ $\frac{8}{13}$ $\frac{2}{3}$ $\frac{9}{12}$
54	$\frac{2}{7}$ $\frac{1}{3}$ $\frac{3}{5}$ $\frac{9}{11}$ $\frac{5}{6}$
55	$\frac{2}{10}$ $\frac{3}{7}$ $\frac{4}{5}$ $\frac{7}{8}$ $\frac{8}{8}$
56	$1088\frac{3}{4}$
57	$656\frac{1}{4}$
58	$1137\frac{4}{5}$
59	$815\frac{1}{3}$
60	$1387\frac{2}{3}$
61	1, 2, 3, 6, 9, 18, 27, 54
62	1, 2, 4, 7, 14, 28
63	1, 2, 3, 4, 6, 7, 12, 14, 21, 28, 42, 84
64	63, 126, 189, 252, 315
65	87, 174, 261, 348, 435
66	£33.75
67	£175.50
68	£9720
69	£30
70	£60
71	840 km
72	1524 km
73	2352 km
74	3300 km
75	6336 km
76	2100
77	1200
78	1400
79	1300
80	0400

Paper 21 – *continued*

81	£15 250
82	$149\frac{1}{3}$ km
83	32
84	4702 kg
85	£73.10
86–90	Nets C, F, G, H and J should be marked.
91	DCXLVIII
92	CDV
93	MCXLVIII
94	MDCCCLXXX
95	MMLXXII
96	$\frac{1}{8}$
97	2
98	$\frac{2}{5}$
99	3
100	$\frac{3}{10}$

Progress Paper 22

1	2 h 36 min
2	1043
3	1 h 6 min
4	0845 (0635 is Saturdays only)
5	38 min
6	990 m
7	5221
8	2432 km
9	1626
10	3405
11	43 000 rupees
12	2 100 000 000
13	12 000 000 000
14	2 879 982 000
15	7 500 000 000
16	N
17	X
18	S
19	H
20	O

(Answers may be in any order)

21	1.08
22	6.2
23	2.4
24	0.02
25	0.04
26	$6\frac{24}{25}$
27	$22\frac{17}{20}$
28	$50\frac{33}{50}$
29	$7\frac{2}{25}$
30	$18\frac{6}{25}$
31	310 miles
32	120 miles
33	380 miles
34	980 miles
35	156 miles
36	0154
37	1642
38	2333
39	0640
40	1847

Paper 22 – continued

41	2
42	4
43	6
44	5
45	9

	kg	g
46	275	0
47	1200	0
48	19	950
49	130	0
50	213	200

51–55

$\frac{5}{12}$	$\frac{1}{3}$	$\frac{3}{4}$
$\frac{5}{6}$	$\frac{1}{2}$	$\frac{1}{6}$
$\frac{1}{4}$	$\frac{2}{3}$	$\frac{7}{12}$

56	£90
57	£180
58	£108
59	£300
60	£225
61	0.438
62	0.364
63	0.249
64	186
65	0.34
66	173.618
67	136.574
68	77.2032
69	12 184.2
70	0.0000384
71	100
72	$72\frac{1}{4}$
73	1000
74	$1\frac{1}{2}$
75	370
76	8 cm
77	12 cm
78	10 cm
79	16 m
80	18 m

Paper 22 – *continued*

81	£267 540
82	470 m 25 cm
83	14 l 975 ml
84	3 min 15 s
85	468 kg 125 g

86–90

0.6	2.0	1.0
1.6	1.2	0.8
1.4	0.4	1.8

91	45.8
92	865.2
93	34.6
94	254.0
95	574.7
96	7.6
97	10.4
98	13.3
99	15.6
100	19.8

This book of answers is a pull-out section from
Progress Papers in Mathematics 3

First published in 1994
Revised edition published in 2014
Copyright © Schofield & Sims Ltd 2014

Author: Patrick Berry
Revised by Rebecca Brant and Peter Hall
Patrick Berry has asserted his moral right under the Copyright, Designs and Patents
Act, 1988, to be identified as the author of this work.

Design by **Ledgard Jepson Ltd**

Printed in the UK by **Wyndeham Gait Ltd**, Grimsby, Lincolnshire

ISBN 978 07217 4677 7

British Library Catalogue in Publication Data:
A catalogue record for this book is available from the British Library.

MARK
✓ or ✗

Q. 66–70

capacity
problems

66 How many 25-ml perfume bottles can be filled from a container holding $12\frac{1}{2}$ litres? _____ | 66 ☐

67 If a million-litre storage tank is only $\frac{3}{8}$ full, how many more litres could it hold? _____ l | 67 ☐

68 The residents of Grange Road shower before breakfast, using 3510 litres of water each day. If each resident uses 54 litres of water on average, how many people live on the lane? _____ | 68 ☐

69 If a car travels 64 km on 4 litres of petrol, how far will it travel on 50 ml of petrol? _____ m | 69 ☐

70 How many quarter-litre bottles could be filled from five dozen 50-litre drums? _____ | 70 ☐

Q. 71–75

perimeters

71 A regular octagon has a perimeter of 960 cm. How long is one of its sides? _____ cm | 71 ☐

72 What is the total length of the edges of a 7-cm cube? _____ cm | 72 ☐

73 What is the total length of the edges of a 9-cm cube? _____ cm | 73 ☐

74 How many metres longer is the perimeter of a 3-metre square than the perimeter of a 1-metre square? _____ m | 74 ☐

75 Fence panels cost £6 each and are one metre long. The bill for fencing the perimeter of a playground is £1164. What is the perimeter of the playground? _____ m | 75 ☐

Q. 76–80

area
problems

76 Find the area of a strip of carpet $7\frac{1}{4}$ m long and $1\frac{3}{4}$ m wide. _____ m² | 76 ☐

77 How many square metres are there in 200 000 cm²? _____ m² | 77 ☐

78 A square of coloured card with sides 25 cm long costs 50p. How much will it cost me to cover an area $1\frac{1}{2}$ m square? £ _____ | 78 ☐

79 What is the total surface area of a 3-cm cube? _____ cm² | 79 ☐

80 What is the total surface area of a 6-cm cube? _____ cm² | 80 ☐

Q. 81–85

negative
numbers

Work out the number of years between these BCE and CE dates.

81 63 BCE to CE 19 _____ years | 81 ☐

82 123 BCE to CE 49 _____ years | 82 ☐

83 160 BCE to CE 284 _____ years | 83 ☐

84 349 BCE to CE 765 _____ years | 84 ☐

85 1170 BCE to CE 1390 _____ years | 85 ☐

MARK ☐

Q. 86–90

area of shapes

From the information given, work out the height of each triangle.

	BASE	HEIGHT	AREA	
86	4 m	_____ m	10 m²	86
87	3 cm	_____ cm	9 cm²	87
88	7 cm	_____ cm	14 cm²	88
89	9 cm	_____ cm	$49\frac{1}{2}$ cm²	89
90	12 m	_____ m	66 m²	90

Q. 91–95

Venn diagrams

Fifty farmers were contacted and asked what animals they kept – cows, sheep or hens. Enter the following information in the Venn diagram.

91 Fifteen farmers said that they concentrated solely on beef or milk production.

92 Eleven solely produced eggs and chicken.

93 Eight were Yorkshire hill farmers and earned their living entirely from wool production.

94 a) Five produced both beef and eggs.
b) Three produced chicken and lamb.

95 a) Seven reared cattle and flocks.
b) Only one farmer had all three animals on his farm.

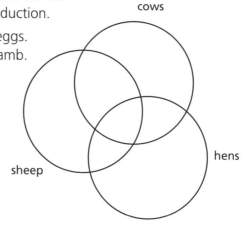

91

92

93

94

95

Q. 96–100

currency conversion

Use the currency conversion table below to work out the following questions:

GB pound	US dollar	South African rand	Brazilian real	Kenyan shilling
£1	$1.5	R16	R$3.7	KSh130

96 How many US dollars would you get for £17? $ _____ | 96

97 Which is greater in value, R$74 or KSh2470? _____ | 97

98 I bought a pair of trainers costing R568. How much is this in GB pounds? £ _____ | 98

99 I have KSh2080. How many US dollars would that buy me? $ _____ | 99

100 How many South African rand could I buy for R$92.50? R _____ | 100

END OF TEST

TOTAL ☐

Mathematics Progress Paper 20

MARK
✓ or ✗

Q. 1–5

pie charts

A small school takes delivery of 144 maths books and distributes them among 5 classes. Use your protractor to work out how many books are delivered to each class.

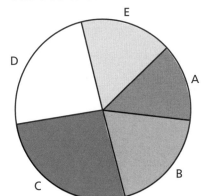

1 Class A: _____ books | 1 ☐

2 Class B: _____ books | 2 ☐

3 Class C: _____ books | 3 ☐

4 Class D: _____ books | 4 ☐

5 Class E: _____ books | 5 ☐

Q. 6–10

writing large numbers

Write down these numbers in figures.

6 eight and three-tenths million   _____ | 6 ☐

7 seven and three-eights million   _____ | 7 ☐

8 fifteen and three-quarters million   _____ | 8 ☐

9 nineteen and one-twentieth million   _____ | 9 ☐

10 thirty-two and three-fifths million   _____ | 10 ☐

Q. 11–15

decimal multiplication

11 $3.52 \times 1000 =$ _____ | 11 ☐

12 $469 \times 0.001 =$ _____ | 12 ☐

13 $6.428 \times 12 =$ _____ | 13 ☐

14 $73.2 \times 1.1 =$ _____ | 14 ☐

15 $276.042 \times 1.2 =$ _____ | 15 ☐

Q. 16–20

algebra

If $a = 9$, what is b?

16 $a + b = 13$ _____ | 16 ☐

17 $a + b = 18$ _____ | 17 ☐

18 $2a + b = 20$ _____ | 18 ☐

19 $2a + b = 25$ _____ | 19 ☐

20 $3a + b = 50$ _____ | 20 ☐

MARK ☐

MARK
✓ or ✗

Q. 21–25

area
problems

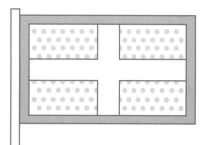

The flag measures 70 cm x 40 cm.
The width of the blue border around the
perimeter of the flag is 5 cm and the
width of the white cross is 10 cm.

21	What is the area of the blue border of the flag in cm²?	_____ cm²	21
22	What is the area of the white cross in cm²?	_____cm²	22
23	What is the area of one of the dotted sections in cm²?	_____ cm²	23
24	What is the area of the entire flag in m²?	_____ m²	24
25	How many flags could be made from 4 m² of fabric?	_____	25

Q. 26–30

measures
addition and
subtraction

26	6 h 4 min + 380 min + 425 min =	_____ h _____ min	26
27	38 g + 216 g + $2\frac{1}{4}$ kg + 9 g + 46 g =	_____ kg _____ g	27
28	$2\frac{4}{5}$ km − 9000 cm =	_____ km _____ m	28
29	£30 000 − £18 442.31 =	£_____	29
30	$300\frac{33}{50}$ l − $201\frac{11}{20}$ l =	_____ l _____ ml	30

Q. 31–35

using money

These are the tickets sold for a concert. Work out the total for each line so that
they all add up to the total given.

April 4th, seats sold for concert	£	P
31	327 seats at £1.25 each		
32	248 seats at £2.50 each		
33	152 seats at £5 each		
34	207 seats at £6.50 each		
35	188 seats at £8.15 each		
Total	4 666	45

| 31 |
| 32 |
| 33 |
| 34 |
| 35 |

MARK [   ]

MARK
✓ or ✗

Q. 36–40

coordinates

Give the coordinates of the middle of each shape.
Use your ruler to help you.

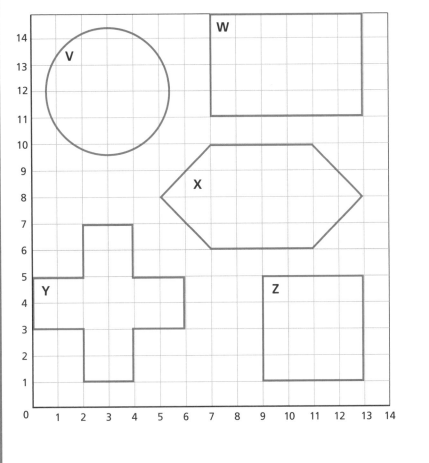

36	37	38
Shape V _____ , _____	Shape W _____ , _____	Shape X _____ , _____

39	40
Shape Y _____ , _____	Shape Z _____ , _____

36 ☐
37 ☐
38 ☐
39 ☐
40 ☐

Q. 41–45

money
problems

41 Divide £45 135 by fifty-nine.   £ _____

42 27 school computers cost a total of £17 658 to replace.
How much is this each?   £ _____

43 A car rental company replaces 9 cars at a total cost of
£76 770. How much is this per vehicle?   £ _____

44 An estate agent sold 12 identical houses for £1 037 400.
How much did each house cost?   £ _____

45 A quarter of a million toys were bought by a chain of
toy shops for £2 500 000. How much was this per toy?   £ _____

41 ☐
42 ☐
43 ☐
44 ☐
45 ☐

MARK ☐

MARK
✓ or ✗

Q. 46–50

fractions to percentages

Change each of these fractions to a percentage.

46 $6\frac{6}{20}$ _____ % 46 ☐

47 $9\frac{7}{8}$ _____ % 47 ☐

48 $7\frac{2}{3}$ _____ % 48 ☐

49 5 _____ % 49 ☐

50 $12\frac{12}{25}$ _____ % 50 ☐

Q. 51–55

graphs

On this graph, the solid line shows the mean monthly temperatures in Mallorca. The dashed line shows the mean monthly temperatures in Britain.

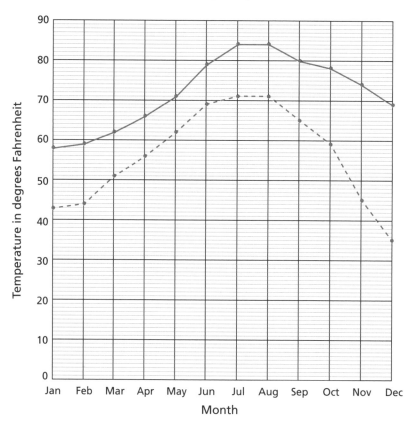

51 July and August are the hottest months in both countries, but how much higher is the mean temperature in Mallorca? _____ °F 51 ☐

52 What is the difference in mean temperature between the two countries in January? _____ °F 52 ☐

53 What is the difference between the highest and the lowest mean monthly temperatures in Mallorca? _____ °F 53 ☐

54 How many months in Mallorca have a mean temperature above 70°F? _____ 54 ☐

55 In the month when Britain has a mean temperature of 45°F, what is the mean temperature in Mallorca? _____ °F 55 ☐

MARK ☐

MARK
✓ or ✗

Q. 56–60

time problems

Here are the flying times between some major cities, given in hours and minutes. For example, the flying time between Beijing and Delhi is 6 h 40 min.

Beijing																
28.31	Buenos Aires															
13.15	20.40	Cairo														
15.15	15.40	18.40	Chicago													
6.40	26.20	7.00	20.05	Delhi												
3.00	29.35	10.55	17.05	6.05	Hong Kong											
15.40	18.45	2.00	12.20	7.35	17.35	Istanbul										
20.10	12.30	8.55	21.40	23.45	14.55	16.30	Johannesburg									
18.05	16.35	5.35	8.30	10.35	16.05	3.50	13.10	London								
15.25	13.45	21.00	5.00	19.30	15.50	14.50	24.10	11.00	Los Angeles							
27.30	16.00	12.35	2.20	17.35	23.05	10.15	20.10	7.00	6.40	Montreal						
8.40	22.05	5.25	12.15	7.35	18.00	4.40	13.30	3.45	14.45	10.45	Moscow					
16.00	24.55	4.55	17.00	10.45	12.45	7.15	3.45	8.30	19.30	15.30	12.50	Nairobi				
16.35	15.35	5.05	9.00	10.45	16.40	3.10	15.50	1.05	12.50	6.25	4.00	9.20	Paris			
11.15	25.20	17.10	23.00	9.30	8.15	15.25	14.20	21.55	19.30	26.30	19.40	23.00	21.40	Perth		
16.15	20.45	17.20	21.10	13.50	10.35	18.40	31.50	11.50	18.10	24.50	19.40	31.35	25.05	23.50	Sydney	
3.50	28.30	19.40	12.55	9.45	4.20	14.05	25.00	11.55	11.55	18.55	9.25	19.55	16.45	17.40	9.15	Tokyo
25.50	11.00	14.20	1.45	20.10	24.15	11.25	21.20	8.10	5.25	2.50	12.30	17.10	12.40	12.40	23.35	12.40	Washington

How long does it take to fly between:

56 Paris and Chicago? _____ h _____ min **56** ☐

57 Moscow and London? _____ h _____ min **57** ☐

58 Sydney and Istanbul? _____ h _____ min **58** ☐

59 Washington and Los Angeles? _____ h _____ min **59** ☐

60 Perth and Montreal? _____ h _____ min **60** ☐

Q. 61–65

time = distance ÷ speed

From the distance and speed given, work out the time taken.

	DISTANCE TRAVELLED	SPEED	TIME TAKEN	
61	50 metres	60 km/h	_____ s	**61** ☐
62	$427\frac{1}{2}$ kilometres	90 km/h	_____ h	**62** ☐
63	7475 kilometres	1150 km/h	_____ h	**63** ☐
64	817 000 metres	76 km/h	_____ h	**64** ☐
65	60 kilometres	8000 m per day	_____ d	**65** ☐

Q. 66–70

ordering decimals

Write the following decimals in order, starting with the smallest.

66 0.067 0.0764 0.0076 0.6 0.67 _____ **66** ☐

67 0.3 0.33 0.303 0.03 0.033 _____ **67** ☐

68 0.51 0.501 0.15 0.115 0.515 _____ **68** ☐

69 0.23 0.293 0.392 0.329 0.32 _____ **69** ☐

70 0.85 0.845 0.853 0.484 0.89 _____ **70** ☐

MARK ☐

MARK
✓ or ✗

Q. 71–75

negative numbers

71 45 − 76 = _____ | 71 ☐

72 29 − 48 = _____ | 72 ☐

73 12 − 83 = _____ | 73 ☐

74 51 − 105 = _____ | 74 ☐

75 36 − 124 = _____ | 75 ☐

Q. 76–80

sequences

Write the next two terms in each of these sequences.

76 $\frac{3125}{32}$ $\frac{625}{16}$ $\frac{125}{8}$ $\frac{25}{4}$ _____ _____ | 76 ☐

77 1   16   81   256   _____ _____ | 77 ☐

78 28   20   12   4   _____ _____ | 78 ☐

79 XV   XXIII   XXXI   XXXIX   _____ _____ | 79 ☐

80 10.6   24.4   38.2   52   _____ _____ | 80 ☐

Q. 81–85

proportion

81 Two-thirds of a lesson lasted 40 minutes. How long was the lesson? _____ min | 81 ☐

82 If 0.5 of a sum of money is £17, find 0.2 of it. £ _____ | 82 ☐

83 The Earth turns 360 degrees in a day. How many degrees does it turn in 20 hours? _____ ° | 83 ☐

84 Nine pencils cost £1.62. How much would 150 cost? £ _____ | 84 ☐

85 5 cm on a map represents a distance of 200 km. What distance would be represented by $7\frac{1}{4}$ cm? _____ km | 85 ☐

Q. 86–90

ratio

86 Divide £2.40 in the ratio of 1 : 7. _____ p and _____ p | 86 ☐

87 Divide 11.25 metres in the ratio of 8 : 1. _____ m and _____ m | 87 ☐

88 Divide £51.15 in the ratio of 7 : 3 : 1.

£ _____ : £ _____ : £ _____ | 88 ☐

89 Divide 28.2 kg in the ratio of 6 : 4 : 2.

_____ kg _____ g : _____ kg _____ g : _____ kg _____ g | 89 ☐

90 Divide 81 km 400 m in the ratio of 8 : 3.

_____ km _____ m : _____ km _____ m | 90 ☐

MARK ☐

MARK
✓ or ✗

Q. 91–95

angles and degrees

91 How many degrees are there in each angle of an equilateral triangle? _____ ° 91 ☐

92 If a ship changes course from north west to north east, through how many degrees will it turn? _____ ° 92 ☐

93 Two angles of a triangle are $38\frac{1}{2}$ degrees and $46\frac{1}{2}$ degrees. What is the third angle? _____ ° 93 ☐

94 How many degrees does the minute hand of a clock pass through in three minutes? _____ ° 94 ☐

95 How many degrees does the second hand of a clock pass through in one minute? _____ ° 95 ☐

Q. 96–100

volume

Here are ten cuboids. Each is identified by a letter. Write down the five pairs which have equal volumes. All measurements are in centimetres.

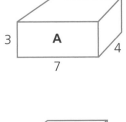
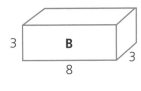
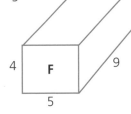
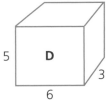
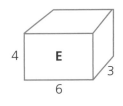
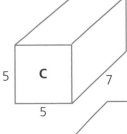
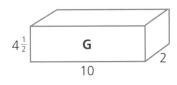
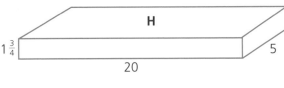
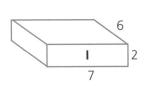
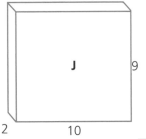

96 _____ and _____

97 _____ and _____

98 _____ and _____

99 _____ and _____

100 _____ and _____

96 ☐
97 ☐
98 ☐
99 ☐
100 ☐

END OF TEST

TOTAL ☐

Mathematics Progress Paper 21

MARK ✓ or ✗

Q. 1–5

rounding

1 Round 1 123 647 to the nearest 1000. _____ | 1 ☐

2 Round 456 819 to the nearest 10 000. _____ | 2 ☐

3 Round 4 572 623 to the nearest 100. _____ | 3 ☐

4 Round 623 833 to the nearest 10 000. _____ | 4 ☐

5 Round 9 478 742 to the nearest 100 000. _____ | 5 ☐

Q. 6–10

fraction addition and subtraction

6 $18\frac{3}{4} + 17\frac{4}{5} + 11\frac{9}{10} =$ _____ | 6 ☐

7 $6\frac{15}{16} + 13\frac{7}{8} + 12\frac{11}{12} =$ _____ | 7 ☐

8 $14\frac{8}{9} + 11\frac{2}{3} + 7\frac{7}{12} =$ _____ | 8 ☐

9 $5\frac{1}{8} - 3\frac{19}{24} =$ _____ | 9 ☐

10 $17\frac{11}{15} - 2\frac{1}{3} - 5\frac{3}{5} =$ _____ | 10 ☐

Q. 11–15

measures conversion

11 Convert 7.06 kilograms to grams. _____ g | 11 ☐

12 Convert 4.003 litres to millilitres. _____ ml | 12 ☐

13 Convert 8.09 km to metres. _____ m | 13 ☐

14 Convert 11.48 kg to grams. _____ g | 14 ☐

15 Convert 3.5 days to minutes. _____ min | 15 ☐

Q. 16–20

magic squares

Fill in the missing numbers so that all the lines, down, across and diagonal, add up to the same number.

14		12	1
11	2		8
5	16	3	
4	9		

16 ☐
17 ☐
18 ☐
19 ☐
20 ☐

MARK ☐

MARK
✓ or ✗

Q. 21–25

area of
shapes

Find the area of the shapes below.

21

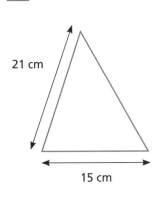

21 cm

15 cm

_____ cm²

22

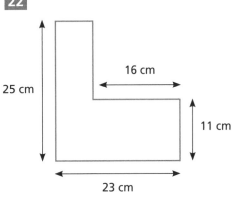

25 cm

16 cm

11 cm

23 cm

_____ cm²

23

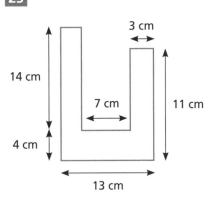

3 cm

14 cm

7 cm

11 cm

4 cm

13 cm

_____ cm²

24

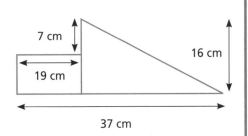

7 cm

19 cm

16 cm

37 cm

_____ cm²

25

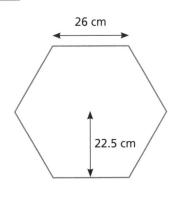

26 cm

22.5 cm

_____ cm²

21 ☐

22 ☐

23 ☐

24 ☐

25 ☐

MARK ☐

MARK
✓ or ✗

Q. 26–30

long division

26

$38\overline{)14\ 706}$

27

$25\overline{)21\ 550}$

28

$52\overline{)37\ 960}$

29

$43\overline{)26\ 273}$

30

$23\overline{)63\ 572}$

26	☐
27	☐
28	☐
29	☐
30	☐

Q. 31–35

greater, equals and less than

Use the signs <, >, or = to complete the following.

31 $\frac{4}{7}$ _____ $\frac{3}{5}$

32 $\frac{13}{24}$ _____ $\frac{4}{9}$

33 $\frac{7}{11}$ _____ $\frac{12}{18}$

34 $\frac{5}{9}$ _____ $\frac{15}{27}$

35 $\frac{16}{14}$ _____ $\frac{8}{7}$

31	☐
32	☐
33	☐
34	☐
35	☐

Q. 36–40

scale

This diagram shows Mrs Sharma's property on the corner of Oaktree Drive and Cedar Avenue. The shaded area is the garden, with Mrs Sharma's house in the middle.

Scale 1cm =10m

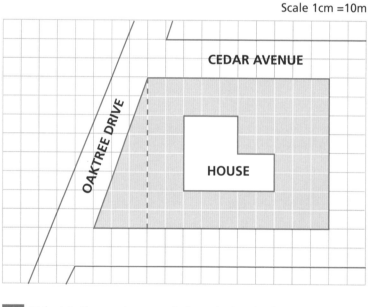

36 What is the perimeter of the whole plot? _____ m

37 What is the perimeter of the area occupied by the house? _____ m

38 What is the area of the whole plot? (A dotted line has been drawn to help you.) _____ m²

39 What is the area of the land occupied by the house? _____ m²

40 What is the area of the garden? _____ m²

36	☐
37	☐
38	☐
39	☐
40	☐

MARK ☐

MARK
✓ or ✗

Q. 41–45

money
problems

41 A new sofa costs £700. If I decide to buy it with £100
deposit and 24 monthly payments of £32.40,
how much extra will it cost me? £ _____ | 41 ☐

42 All 64 seats on a bus are full and each passenger
pays £4.30 for the journey. How much money is
collected altogether? £ _____ | 42 ☐

43 If a shop buys a DVD player for £86 and sells it for
£143, how much profit will be made if 52 DVD players
are sold? £ _____ | 43 ☐

44 How much is thirty-seven-and-a-half times £18.56? £ _____ | 44 ☐

45 If a crate holds a dozen cartons of washing powder
and each carton costs £4.40, how much money will
the owner of the shop take if she sells $8\frac{2}{3}$ crates? £ _____ | 45 ☐

Q. 46–50

estimation
and
approximation

Estimate the answers to these questions by approximating. Underline the answer.
Do not try to work out the exact answer.

46	$99 \times 199 =$	19 000	21 000	18 500	20 000	20 500

46 ☐

47	$538 \div 18 =$	27	33	26	28	30

47 ☐

48	$396 \times 58 =$	20 000	24 000	30 000	26 000	18 000

48 ☐

49	$3807 \div 37 =$	80	50	70	100	120

49 ☐

50	$831 \times 96 =$	60 000	50 000	70 000	90 000	80 000

50 ☐

Q. 51–55

ordering
fractions

Write the following fractions in order, starting with the smallest.

51 $\frac{3}{7}$ $\frac{2}{5}$ $\frac{4}{5}$ $\frac{2}{9}$ $\frac{5}{8}$ _____ | 51 ☐

52 $\frac{2}{7}$ $\frac{8}{11}$ $\frac{3}{4}$ $\frac{2}{6}$ $\frac{7}{10}$ _____ | 52 ☐

53 $\frac{4}{7}$ $\frac{9}{12}$ $\frac{8}{13}$ $\frac{2}{3}$ $\frac{4}{8}$ _____ | 53 ☐

54 $\frac{1}{3}$ $\frac{5}{6}$ $\frac{2}{7}$ $\frac{9}{11}$ $\frac{3}{5}$ _____ | 54 ☐

55 $\frac{8}{9}$ $\frac{2}{10}$ $\frac{4}{5}$ $\frac{7}{8}$ $\frac{3}{7}$ _____ | 55 ☐

Q. 56–60

division with
remainders

Write the answers with the remainders as fractions.

56 ☐

56 $8710 \div 8 =$ _____   **57** $7875 \div 12 =$ _____ | 57 ☐

58 ☐

58 $5689 \div 5 =$ _____   **59** $4892 \div 6 =$ _____ | 59 ☐

60 $12489 \div 9 =$ _____ | 60 ☐

MARK ☐

MARK
✓ or ✗

Q. 61–65

factors and
multiples

61 List all the factors of 54. _____ 61 ☐

62 List all the factors of 28. _____ 62 ☐

63 List all the factors of 84. _____ 63 ☐

64 List the first 5 multiples of 63. _____ 64 ☐

65 List the first 5 multiples of 87. _____ 65 ☐

Q. 66–70

percentage
problems

66 A pair of trousers costing £45 were reduced by 25%.
What was their new price? £ _____ 66 ☐

67 Lara got a 35% discount on a washing machine
costing £270. What price did she pay? £ _____ 67 ☐

68 Jake took out a loan to buy a car. He borrowed £9000
at an interest rate of 8%. How much will he need to
pay back in total? £ _____ 68 ☐

69 Maggie buys a pair at shoes with a discount of 20%.
She pays £24. What was the original price? £ _____ 69 ☐

70 Joel buys a coat for £51 with a discount of 15%.
What was the original price? £ _____ 70 ☐

Q. 71–75

distance =
speed × time

A plane travels at 720 km/h. How far does it fly in:

71 1 h 10 min? _____ km 71 ☐

72 2 h 7 min? _____ km 72 ☐

73 3 h 16 min? _____ km 73 ☐

74 4 h 35 min? _____ km 74 ☐

75 8.8 h? _____ km 75 ☐

MARK ☐

MARK
✓ or ✗

Q. 76–80

time problems

This map shows the time everywhere in the world when it is midday in London, on the Greenwich Meridian.

When it is midday in London, what time is it:

76 in Western Australia? _____ | 76 ☐

77 in North-West Africa? _____ | 77 ☐

78 in South Africa? _____ | 78 ☐

79 in Norway and Sweden? _____ | 79 ☐

80 on the West Coast of the United States? _____ | 80 ☐

Q. 81–85

mean, median, mode and range

81 Find the mean of £17 500, £16 000 and £12 250. £ _____ | 81 ☐

82 In six days a delivery van covered these distances:
112 km, 156 km, 135 km, 201 km, 140 km and 152 km.
What was its mean daily journey? _____ km | 82 ☐

83 A netball team scored 192 points in 6 games.
What was their mean score per game? _____ | 83 ☐

84 Find the mean of 1298 kg, 1530 kg,
6482 kg, 9775 kg and 4425 kg. _____ kg | 84 ☐

85 In four weeks Grace spent £254 at the supermarket.
For the first three weeks she spent a mean of
£60.30 per week. How much did she spend in
the fourth week? £ _____ | 85 ☐

MARK ☐

MARK
✓ or ✗

Q. 86–90

nets

These shapes each have five squares and are called pentominoes. Eight of the twelve will fold up into a cube **without** a lid. Three of these have been indicated with an X below. Put an X under the other five.

A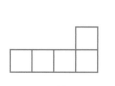

B

C

D

_____ X _____

_____

_____

_____ X _____

E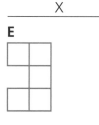

F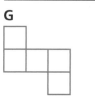

G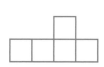

H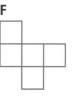

_____

_____

_____

_____

I

J

K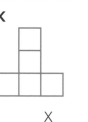

L

_____

_____

_____ X _____

_____

86 ☐

87 ☐

88 ☐

89 ☐

90 ☐

Q. 91–95

Roman numerals

Work out these sums and write the answers in Roman numerals.

91 $18 \times 36 =$ _____

92 $27 \times 15 =$ _____

93 $82 \times 14 =$ _____

94 $94 \times 20 =$ _____

95 $37 \times 56 =$ _____

91 ☐

92 ☐

93 ☐

94 ☐

95 ☐

Q. 96–100

fraction multiplication and division

96 $\frac{1}{2} \times \frac{1}{4} =$ _____

97 $\frac{2}{5} \div \frac{1}{5} =$ _____

98 $\frac{4}{5} \times \frac{1}{2} =$ _____

99 $\frac{3}{4} \div \frac{1}{4} =$ _____

100 $\frac{9}{10} \times \frac{1}{3} =$ _____

96 ☐

97 ☐

98 ☐

99 ☐

100 ☐

END OF TEST

TOTAL ☐

START HERE

Q. 1–5

timetables

This timetable gives details of trains between Leeds and Carlisle.

Monday to Saturday   **SX**=Saturdays excepted **SO**=Saturdays only

		SX	SO			SO							
Leeds		0601	0635	0845	0901	0945	1049	1249	1301	1449	1631	1725	1833
Shipley		0615	0650	0902	0918	1004	1104	1304	1317	1504	1646	1740	1848
Keighley		0623	1658	0913	0932	1012	1112	1312	1331	1512	1659	1753	1902
Skipton	0535	0638	0715	0929	0952	1028	1128	1328	1352	1528	1721	1816	1921
Gargrave	0540				0958	1034			1358		1727	1821	1927
Hellifield	0549				1007	1043			1407		1736	1830	1936
Long Preston	0552				1010	1046			1410		1739	1833	1939
Giggleswick	0559				1017				1417		1746		
Clapham	0608				1025				1425		1754		
Bentham	0614				1032				1432		1801		
Wennington	0619				1036				1436		1805		
Carnforth	0637				1054				1454		1823		
Lancaster	0650				1105				1509		1834		
Morecombe	0710				1125				1608		1924		
Settle		0655	0732	0947		1053	1146	1345		1545		1839	1945
Horton in Ribb		0704	0741	0956		1102	1155	1354		1554		1848	1954
Ribblehead		0712	0749	1004		1110	1203	1402		1602		1856	2003
Dent		0721	1758	1013		1119	1212	1411		1611		1905	
Garsdale		0727	0804	1018		1124	1218	1417		1617		1910	
Kirkby Stephen		0739	0816	1030		1137	1230	1429		1629		1922	
Appleby		0752	0829	1043		1151	1244	1442		1642		1935	
Langwathby		0806	0843	1057		1205	1258	1456		1656		1949	
Lazonby & Kirk		0812	0849	1103		1211	1304	1502		1702		1955	
Armathwaite		0819	1856	1111		1218	1311	1509		1709		2003	
Carlisle	0857	0837	0914	1129	1234	1236	1329	1528	1642	1730	1957	2020	

1 How long does the train leaving Leeds at 0601 take to complete the journey? _____ h _____ min

2 If I board the 0913 at Keighley, at what time will I arrive at Appleby? _____

3 I leave the 0845 train at Ribblehead. How long do I have to go walking before the next train? _____ h _____ min

4 One Friday I decide to visit the Appleby cricket ground. I want to be there as soon as possible after 0800. Which train should I catch from Leeds? _____

5 How much slower is the 0901 from Leeds to Carlisle than the 1725? _____ min

1 ☐
2 ☐
3 ☐
4 ☐
5 ☐

Q. 6–10

multiplication problems

6 If street lamps are positioned every 55 metres, what distance will be needed to place 19 lamps? _____ m

7 A bookseller, open 7 days each week, averaged 58 sales each day in August, 49 in September and 63 in October. How many books did he sell altogether? _____

8 From Sheffield to Doncaster is 32 km. If a bus covers the return journey twice on a Sunday and six times every other day, how many km does it cover in a week? _____ km

9 Cat's-eyes are positioned every four metres down the centre of a $6\frac{1}{2}$ km road. How many are needed? _____

10 To the square of 19 add the product of 20 and 16 and multiply the result by five. _____

6 ☐
7 ☐
8 ☐
9 ☐
10 ☐

MARK ☐

MARK
✓ or ✗

Q. 11–15

large number
problems

11 If 86 rupees equal £1, how many rupees equal £500? _____ rupees   11 ☐

12 Multiply seventy million by thirty. _____   12 ☐

13 What is the product of 20 million and 6 hundred? _____   13 ☐

14 The population of China is 1 353 821 000.
The population of the USA is 315 968 000 and that
of India 1 210 193 000. What is the population of these
three countries? _____   14 ☐

15 Write in figures seven and a half billion. _____   15 ☐

Q. 16–20

symmetry

If certain shapes or letters fit their outlines when given a half turn (180°)
about their centres, then they have half-symmetry. Which five of the letters
below have half-symmetry?

B N X T U W
S H E M O

16 _____ 17 _____ 18 _____ 19 _____ 20 _____

16 ☐
17 ☐
18 ☐
19 ☐
20 ☐

Q. 21–25

decimal
division

Write each answer as a decimal.

21 What is 9.72 divided by 9? _____   21 ☐

22 What is 6.82 divided by 1.1? _____   22 ☐

23 What is 12 000 divided by 5000? _____   23 ☐

24 What is 1.2 divided by 60? _____   24 ☐

25 What is 24 divided by 600? _____   25 ☐

Q. 26–30

reduce to
lowest terms

Write these decimals as fractions in their lowest terms.

26 6.96 _____   26 ☐

27 22.85 _____   27 ☐

28 50.66 _____   28 ☐

29 7.08 _____   29 ☐

30 18.24 _____   30 ☐

MARK ☐

MARK
✓ or ✗

Q. 31–35

length problems

Leeds															
73	Liverpool														
40	35	Manchester													
91	152	128	Newcastle upon Tyne												
172	215	185	255	Norwich											
65	95	70	152	125	Nottingham										
160	150	141	242	138	94	Oxford									
375	340	342	465	390	320	250	Penzance								
235	251	251	150	400	295	390	590	Perth							
310	275	276	400	320	252	180	78	525	Plymouth						
56	30	31	122	212	100	170	361	225	302	Preston					
33	72	38	122	142	37	125	346	266	280	68	Sheffield				
222	215	204	312	190	157	65	217	454	145	232	191	Southampton			
215	220	218	151	387	281	355	551	144	490	190	245	421	Stranraer		
24	95	64	81	172	78	171	391	227	331	80	52	234	212	York	
190	195	181	272	112	121	56	280	416	210	212	160	76	393	195	London

This chart shows the distances in miles between various cities in Britain.

31 How far is it from Leeds to Plymouth? _____ miles   31 ☐

32 How much further is it from Liverpool to Oxford than it is from Liverpool to Preston? _____ miles   32 ☐

33 How many miles is the return journey between Leeds and London? _____ miles   33 ☐

34 If I go from Norwich to Penzance and then on to Perth, how many miles will I travel? _____ miles   34 ☐

35 If I live halfway between Newcastle upon Tyne and Southampton, how far am I from Southampton? _____ miles   35 ☐

Q. 36–40

24-hour clock

Change these times to 24-hour times.

36 six minutes to two in the morning   _____   36 ☐

37 eighteen minutes to five in the afternoon   _____   37 ☐

38 twenty-seven minutes to midnight   _____   38 ☐

39 forty minutes past six in the morning   _____   39 ☐

40 thirteen minutes before seven in the evening   _____   40 ☐

Q. 41–45

algebra

Find the value of x if:

41 $3x + 7 = 8x - 3$ $x =$ _____   41 ☐

42 $2x + 9 = 5x - 3$ $x =$ _____   42 ☐

43 $5x + 4 = 8x - 14$ $x =$ _____   43 ☐

44 $4x - 7 = 2x + 3$ $x =$ _____   44 ☐

45 $6x - 12 = 4x + 6$ $x =$ _____   45 ☐

MARK ☐

MARK
✓ or ✗

Q. 46–50

mass problems

Work out the masses of these items so that they all add up to the total given.

		kg	g
46	550 packets of rice at 500 g each		
47	1200 packets of sugar at 1 kg each		
48	70 jars of honey at 285 g each		
49	650 packets of biscuits at 200 g each		
50	520 frozen pizzas at 410 g each		
	Total	1 8 3 8	1 5 0

46 ☐
47 ☐
48 ☐
49 ☐
50 ☐

Q. 51–55

magic squares: fractions

Enter the missing fractions in this magic square so that all the lines, across, down and diagonal, add up to the same number.

$\frac{5}{12}$	$\frac{1}{3}$	
	$\frac{1}{2}$	
		$\frac{7}{12}$

51 ☐
52 ☐
53 ☐
54 ☐
55 ☐

Q. 56–60

unequal sharing

56 Share £210 among 3 people so that one gets $1\frac{1}{2}$ times as much as each of the others. How much is the largest share?   £ _____

57 Share £340 among 3 people so that one gets $2\frac{1}{4}$ times as much as each of the others. How much is the largest share?   £ _____

58 Share £198 among 3 people so that one gets $2\frac{2}{5}$ times as much as each of the others. How much is the largest share?   £ _____

59 Share £460 among 3 people so that one gets $3\frac{3}{4}$ times as much as each of the others. How much is the largest share?   £ _____

60 Share £465 among 3 people so that one gets $1\frac{7}{8}$ times as much as each of the others. How much is the largest share?   £ _____

56 ☐
57 ☐
58 ☐
59 ☐
60 ☐

Q. 61–65

decimal long division

61 $0.00657 \div 0.015 =$ _____

62 $0.10192 \div 0.28 =$ _____

63 $1.5189 \div 6.1 =$ _____

64 $65.1 \div 0.35 =$ _____

65 $0.0884 \div 0.26 =$ _____

61 ☐
62 ☐
63 ☐
64 ☐
65 ☐

MARK ☐

MARK
✓ or ✗

Q. 66–70

decimal long multiplication

66
$$36.94$$
$$\times\ 4.7$$
_____
_____

67
$$593.8$$
$$\times\ 0.23$$
_____
_____

68
$$8.042$$
$$\times\ 9.6$$
_____
_____

69 $193.4 \times 63 =$ _____

70 $0.00024 \times 0.16 =$ _____

66 ☐
67 ☐
68 ☐
69 ☐
70 ☐

Q. 71–75

square numbers and roots

71 How many less than 1000 is the square of 30? _____

72 What is the square of $8\frac{1}{2}$? _____

73 What is the square root of a million? _____

74 Divide the square root of 144 by the square root of 64. _____

75 To the square of 9 add the square of 17. _____

71 ☐
72 ☐
73 ☐
74 ☐
75 ☐

Q. 76–80

area of shapes

From the figures given, work out the length of the base of each triangle.

	BASE	HEIGHT	AREA
76	_____ cm	8 cm	32 cm²
77	_____ cm	9 cm	54 cm²
78	_____ cm	16 cm	80 cm²
79	_____ m	40 m	320 m²
80	_____ m	$12\frac{1}{2}$ m	$112\frac{1}{2}$ m²

76 ☐
77 ☐
78 ☐
79 ☐
80 ☐

Q. 81–85

measures multiplication and division

81 £17 836 × 15 = £ _____

82 $42\frac{3}{4}$ m × 11 = _____ m _____ cm

83 $74\frac{7}{8}$ l ÷ 5 = _____ l _____ ml

84 2340 sec ÷ 12 = _____ min _____ s

85 $4213\frac{1}{8}$ kg ÷ 9 = _____ kg _____ g

81 ☐
82 ☐
83 ☐
84 ☐
85 ☐

MARK ☐

MARK
✓ or ✗

Q. 86–90

magic squares

Fill in the missing numbers in this square so that each line, across, down and diagonal, adds up to the same figure.

0.6	2.0	1.0
	1.2	

86 ☐
87 ☐
88 ☐
89 ☐
90 ☐

Q. 91–95

rounding

Round the following numbers to 1 decimal place.

91 45.781 _____

92 865.248 _____

93 34.582 _____

94 253.97 _____

95 574.715 _____

91 ☐
92 ☐
93 ☐
94 ☐
95 ☐

Q. 96–100

number lines

Write the value of each letter as a decimal.

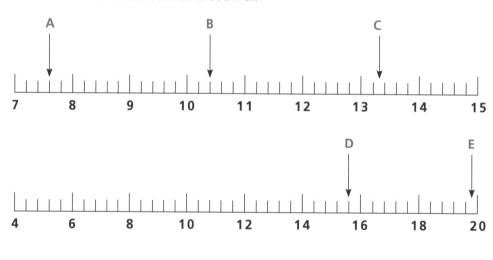

96 A = _____   97 B = _____   98 C = _____

99 D = _____   100 E = _____

96 ☐
97 ☐
98 ☐
99 ☐
100 ☐

END OF TEST

TOTAL ☐

TOPICS COVERED	Paper	Book 1									Book 2						Book 3						
		1	2	3	4	5	6	7	8	9	10	11	12	13	14	15	16	17	18	19	20	21	22
numbers and place value	greater, equals and less than		•																			•	
	negative numbers												•	•						•	•		•
	number lines																		•		•		
	place value	•				•		•					•			•				•			•
	Roman numerals							•					•	•		•				•		•	•
	rounding	•										•						•				•	
	sequences		•		•	•			•			•				•	•				•		
	writing large numbers		•		•	•			•			•	•				•			•	•	•	•
addition, subtraction, multiplication and division	addition and subtraction problems	•	•		•	•		•	•			•			•			•					
	BODMAS			•				•		•				•			•			•			
	cube numbers																•			•		•	
	divisibility rules			•		•								•									
	division problems	•		•	•			•			•							•			•		
	division with remainders								•	•					•			•					
	estimation and approximation			•	•	•	•			•	•						•			•		•	•
	factors and multiples		•	•		•				•		•			•							•	
	large number problems		•	•						•				•	•		•			•		•	•
	long division			•	•	•	•		•				•					•					
	long multiplication		•	•		•				•								•			•		
	magic squares					•		•															
	missing numbers	•		•	•		•			•	•		•		•			•					•
	multiplication problems	•			•		•			•	•				•								•
	prime numbers	•			•								•				•						
	simple addition and subtraction						•			•							•	•	•				
	simple division	•					•			•	•						•	•	•				
	simple multiplication	•				•	•	•			•												
	square numbers and roots	•							•								•			•		•	•
fractions, decimals and percentages	decimal addition and subtraction	•	•	•	•		•	•		•	•	•	•	•	•		•	•		•	•	•	•
	decimal division	•	•	•						•	•	•		•			•	•	•			•	
	decimal long division																		•		•		•
	decimal long multiplication														•				•				•
	decimal multiplication										•		•		•		•				•	•	
	decimal problems	•	•		•				•			•	•			•	•						
	equivalent fractions	•			•		•	•		•			•					•			•		
	fraction addition and subtraction	•	•	•									•		•					•		•	
	fraction multiplication and division	•	•	•											•							•	
	fraction problems	•					•			•			•				•				•		
	fractions to decimals				•														•				
	fractions to percentages		•					•				•		•		•		•				•	
	magic squares: fractions															•							
	ordering decimals																	•			•		
	ordering fractions									•	•	•						•					
	percentage problems	•				•									•					•		•	•
	reduce to lowest terms	•		•				•	•										•				•

TOPICS COVERED	Paper		Book 1								Book 2							Book 3						
		1	2	3	4	5	6	7	8	9	10	11	12	13	14	15	16	17	18	19	20	21	22
ratio and proportion	proportion					●			●	●						●	●				●		
	ratio		●	●		●			●		●		●		●		●				●	●	
	unequal sharing							●				●				●			●				●
algebra	algebra		●	●		●			●				●	●	●	●			●		●		●
	what is my number?	●	●		●	●			●								●		●				
measurement	24-hour clock				●		●				●				●		●			●		●	
	area problems											●			●					●			
	capacity problems			●	●		●				●	●			●		●			●			●
	currency conversion									●					●				●	●			
	distance = speed x time																					●	
	length problems				●	●		●		●		●				●			●	●			
	mass problems									●							●			●			
	measures addition and subtraction	●			●		●	●	●	●			●	●			●				●		
	measures conversion		●		●			●	●	●			●	●	●	●		●	●				
	measures multiplication and division		●	●	●		●	●	●	●	●	●	●	●		●		●	●	●	●		
	metric/imperial conversions									●													
	money problems	●	●		●	●	●	●	●		●		●			●		●			●		●
	speed = distance ÷ time							●	●	●	●			●			●	●		●	●	●	
	time = distance ÷ speed							●	●	●	●						●	●	●		●		
	time problems			●	●					●			●			●	●				●	●	
	using money					●			●				●				●		●		●		
	volume																●	●			●		
properties of shape	angles and degrees			●	●		●	●				●		●	●	●	●				●	●	●
	area of shapes						●	●	●				●		●	●		●				●	
	nets				●		●	●				●				●				●			
	perimeters		●						●										●				
	reflection and rotation		●		●			●	●		●			●		●		●	●	●			
	scale					●					●			●					●				
	shape properties			●	●							●	●		●	●	●	●	●				
	symmetry					●							●	●	●			●	●				
	triangles	●												●	●				●				
position and direction	compass points		●					●	●		●	●			●			●			●		
	coordinates			●					●						●	●	●	●				●	●
	translation						●	●	●			●	●	●	●		●						●
statistics	bar charts	●		●	●	●											●						●
	graphs		●				●		●		●		●						●	●	●		●
	mean, median, mode and range														●								
	pictograms	●																					
	pie charts	●		●			●														●	●	
	timetables				●	●			●			●		●		●	●				●		●
	Venn diagrams	●	●	●																●			●
probability	probability	●	●		●				●						●	●		●		●			●